# WEIGHING YOUR OPTIONS

## A GUIDED WORKBOOK FOR BODY IMAGE AND DISORDERED EATING

### JENNIFER CRAIG, LCSW, BCD

For Dad

# WEIGHING YOUR OPTIONS

## A GUIDED WORKBOOK FOR BODY IMAGE AND DISORDERED EATING

Jennifer Craig, LCSW, BCD

Eau Claire, Wisconsin
2006

PESI, LLC
PO Box 1000
200 Spring Street
Eau Claire, Wisconsin 54702

Illustrations Copyright Mike Hluhan, shovelclothing@aol.com, 412-999-2933
Used with permission

Printed in the United States of America

ISBN: 0-9749711-6-2

For information on this and other PESI manuals and
audio recordings, please call 800-843-7763 or
visit our website at www.pesi.com

# TABLE OF CONTENTS

# Contents

## Contents

# ABOUT THE AUTHOR

**Jenny Craig, LCSW, BCD** is a licensed clinical social worker, educator, consultant, author, and personal coach. She has studied in nine countries and authored the "Love Your Body" column. Jenny has provided trainings across the United States on numerous topics and draws from her outpatient practice as well as years in management positions. Jenny currently owns her own private practice, and owns and operates Training Plus, which provides corporate trainings and consulting with psychological insight. Find out more at www.jennycraigconsulting.com and www.trainingplus.biz.

# AUTHOR'S NOTE

Research demonstrates that the best way to help someone struggling with a disorder is to prevent it from occurring. Enclosed you will find over 100 different ideas in handouts and worksheets to learn to "Drop the Negative Weight" that we carry in our minds. My hope is that therapists, doctors, health teachers, parents, and anyone who has an interest will utilize this workbook with people who seek to find their "healthy weight."

# INTRODUCTION

Welcome weary travelers. I imagine you have been down many roads in your struggles with weight and image. As you go through this book, not everything will apply to you. You are an individual and beautiful in your very own way. Your struggles can be similar to others or very different. This compilation of worksheets was put together for everyone. Be proud of the next steps you take with this workbook. They will not be easy; nothing life changing ever is.

So, what is a normal body? This book is meant to help you clarify your personal definition of a "normal" body. After years of researching this question, I believe the definition of a normal body is where your body functions best. To be at your personal best, it is essential to manage both actions and thoughts. Most of us only focus on our bodies from the neck down, but this workbook seeks to manage the weight we carry around from the neck up—the thought patterns that help keep us stuck in chronic dieting, self-loathing, and/or eating disorders.

Illustration by Mike Hluhan

Let's begin by talking about where you find yourself today. A part of our brain is like a compass, designed to help us find our way around. I sometimes laugh that this part of my brain got lost or at least off course, as I am directionally challenged. Think, for example, about how you travel to work. Most people take the same route every day. Even if the path has more traffic, more hassles, and takes a little longer, it is what they know. It is routine. It is comfortable. Hopefully, through information found in this workbook, you will find the path that is right for you. So, welcome weary travelers, and happy trails.

# EASY STEPS TO A HEALTHY WEIGHT

## PART 1

## THE SECRET TO FINDING YOUR HEALTHY WEIGHT

*"I shut my eyes in order to see."* —Paul Gauguin

The purpose of this book is to help you look inside yourself instead of focusing on the outside. If you listen to your body, it will tell you where it functions best. Every single human being has a homeostatic point or set-point where it functions best with a healthy diet and regular exercise. If you pay attention to your body for a significant amount of time without dieting, binging, or any other unnatural behavior, you will notice that no matter what you do, your body will keep coming back within the same 5 to 10 pounds. Your body does not understand from the neck down why you mentally want to be a certain weight. All your body knows is that it needs to survive. It will work to remain at the weight where you function best. When you are at your set-point, you sleep better, feel better, and have more energy. When you decide to ignore where your body functions best, your sleep, emotions, concentration, and energy are all affected.

So, that is one of the big secrets—your body knows where it functions best. Well, please sit down, because I am about to share THE secret, the secret the diet companies do not want you to know. The secret to losing weight is . . . remain active and make good food choices. Now, don't set the book down yet. I know that you might be discouraged by that answer, but it is true. One of the reasons why it is meant to be kept a secret is that the dieting and weight loss industry makes more than 33 billion dollars a year on our collective continued failures. If we all succeeded in losing the weight we hoped to lose and keeping it off, the diet industry would go out of business, right? I think that you will agree with me when I say there are more diets than you can list, and you may have tried them all. Of all the diets that you have put your body and mind through, have any of them told you what your healthy weight is? Or is this something that you determined for yourself? Do you know what your healthy weight is? Let's take time to tell you the truth. The truth is that there is currently no definitive way to assess where your body functions best. There are, however, several ways to assess your weight (e.g., medical professionals often use charts such as the one seen here and/or your weight circumference).

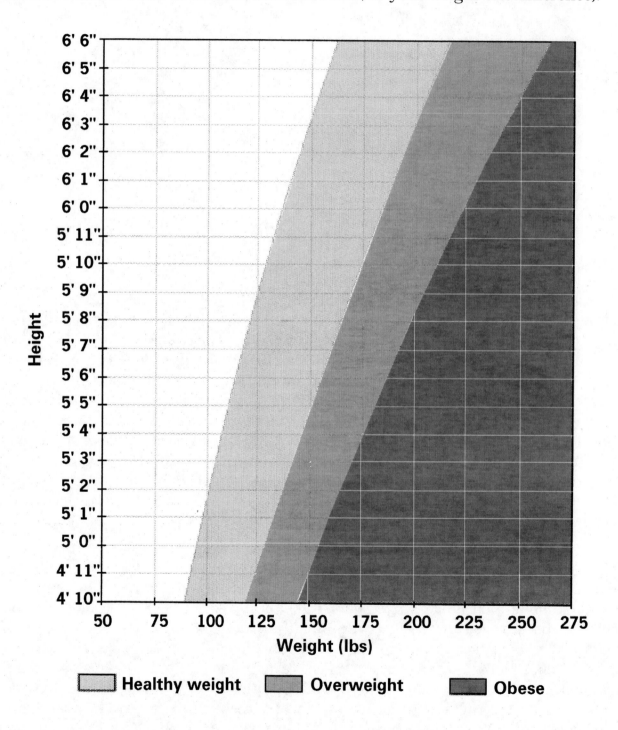

This chart can be used as one way to assess whether or not you fall into the medically healthy category. The problem with using charts is that they do not work for every type of person. For example, if Sylvester Stallone used this chart, he would be considered obese. Most people would disagree if you called Rocky "obese."

The National Institutes of Health (NIH) present another way of determining your medically healthy weight. According to the NIH, you can determine your medical health by doing the following: Get a measuring tape. Measure your waist circumference by placing a tape measure around your body at the level of the uppermost part of your hipbone. (This is usually at the level of your navel.) You are at increased risk for health problems if you are:

- a man with a waist measurement greater than 40 inches (101.6 cm).

- a woman with a waist measurement greater than 35 inches (88.9 cm).

The NIH also recommends calculating your waist-to-hip ratio. To accomplish this, use a tape measure to measure your waist at your bellybutton. Next, measure your hips at their widest point. (Stand with your feet apart, in a relaxed position.) Then divide your waist measurement by your hip measurement. Ideally,

- women want to be at .80 or less.

- men want to be at .95 or less.

These are the medical evaluations used to determine health.

MY MEDICALLY HEALTHY WEIGHT IS _____.

# WHAT IS THE DEFINITION OF HEALTHY WEIGHT?

Now that you have defined your medically healthy weight, let's look at the other definitions of what healthy weight might really mean. Are you managing all areas of your body?

Healthy weight can be defined by: (1) eating the nutrition that your body needs, (2) engaging in regular physical activity, and (3) healthy stress management. If we follow this definition, it makes sense that when we go against what is healthy for our body, our body fights us. From the neck up, we feel we have a very valid reason to go on a crash diet to lose those last 10 vanity pounds for our class reunion. From the neck down, our body does not agree that it is okay to deny our vital organs the nutrients they need in order to impress the people with whom we went to high school. At first, your brain wins the battle, and for one month you go on a crash diet and fit into that outfit that you insisted on wearing. In the end, your body wins. Your weight goes right back to where it was functioning best. No matter our thoughts, the body still functions in survival mode. Your body seeks the weight where you are most in balance. When your body is in balance, you will feel better, sleep better, and be able to concentrate better.

Scientists are working to find answers, but here's what we know so far . . . It's not just a matter of willpower—there's a biological reason why diets don't work.

# MY BODY WON'T DIET

When you restrict how much you eat by dieting, your body says:

- Wait a minute—I listen to my genes, not fashion designers.

- And I need energy to feel good and have fun.

When you diet, your body tries to maintain its natural set-point range by slowing its metabolism. That's the rate at which your body uses up the calories you take in.

- Although it may be easy to lose weight at first, if your target weight (the weight you're trying to reach) is below your natural set-point range, losing further weight becomes more difficult.

- When you give up on a diet, it takes time for your metabolism to return to its natural range.

- During this time, it's easy to regain the weight you lost, and more.

- Most dieters don't consider their body's set-point range and strive for unrealistic target weights.

- Most dieters feel discouraged and guilty when they don't reach their goal.

- They are likely to overeat to make up for feeling deprived of food during dieting.

(Resource: Peel Public Health)

# UH-OH, TIME TO WEIGH YOURSELF . . .

Now that you have defined your medical weight, let us define your negative weight. Negative weight is defined as the mental energy and thought patterns that you use every single day of your life. Negative weight deals with your current emotional relationship with food, self-esteem, and body image. Before we take some time and complete some discovery worksheets, assign yourself your own negative weight. If there were a special scale to weigh just how negative your thoughts about yourself have become and the emotional ties that you have with food, how much would you weigh? (The more negative thoughts and the more emotional ties with food, the higher the number.)

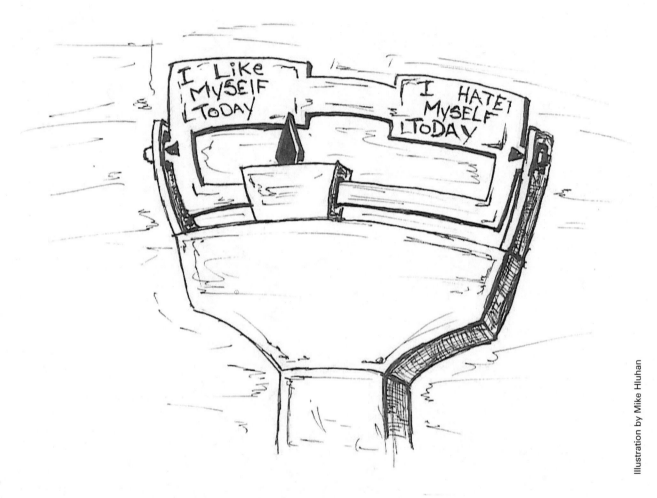

Illustration by Mike Hluhan

MY NEGATIVE WEIGHT IS: _____.

Asking this question of hundreds of people, I have heard very interesting answers. The majority of answers were heavier than people's actual physical weight. As you know if you have ever tried losing your physical weight, it is not easy. I will let you know ahead of time that losing your negative weight is just as challenging. The good news is that when you have taken the time to discover how heavy that negative weight has become, you can begin to lose it. And, when you lose that negative weight, it will change almost every area of your life.

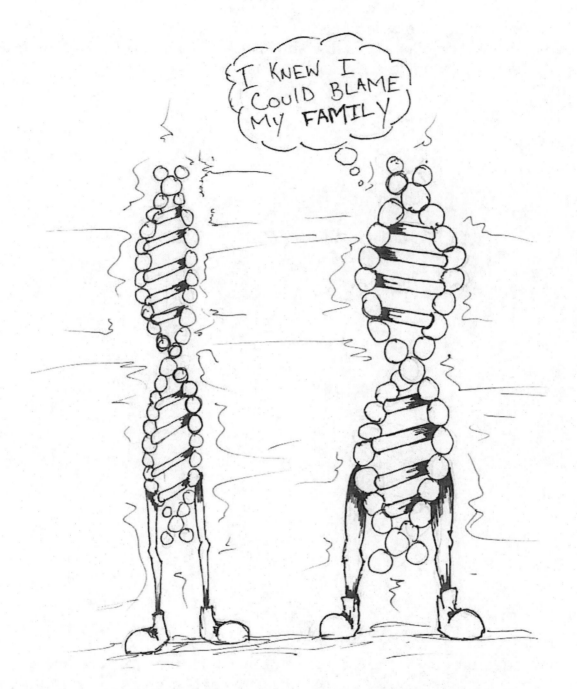

Illustration by Mike Hluhan

# THE REAL SECRETS ABOUT DIETING

The secret is diets do not work. Yes, they can be quite successful for helping individuals lose weight, but for every diet I have run across, there is an end to it. The problem with stopping dieting is that when you stop, you often gain the weight back. Your body wants to go back to its set-point. Is that really a surprise? If you are a natural brunette and get your hair dyed blonde, you will now be a blonde. If you stop dying your hair, you will go back to being a brunette. The point is that any time you want to change, you will have to keep that change going. Diets do not work; lifestyle changes do. So, what do you know so far? You know whether or not you are considered medically overweight. You know that diets do not work. You need to change your lifestyle.

Now let's discuss the major factors affecting people's weight. According to Peel Public Health (www.region.peel.on.ca/health):

- Dieting can make you feel guilty about doing something as natural as eating.

- Diet plans and supplements are often lacking important nutrients needed for health and energy.

- Dieting can throw off body chemistry and fluid balance, along with energy, moods, and concentration.

- In teens, dieting can cause permanent damage, such as loss of normal bone density.

- 95% of people who lose weight by dieting gain the weight back and more!

- Repeated dieting may actually result in an elevated set-point. This means it's possible to start off in a healthy weight range and diet your way up to an unhealthy weight range.

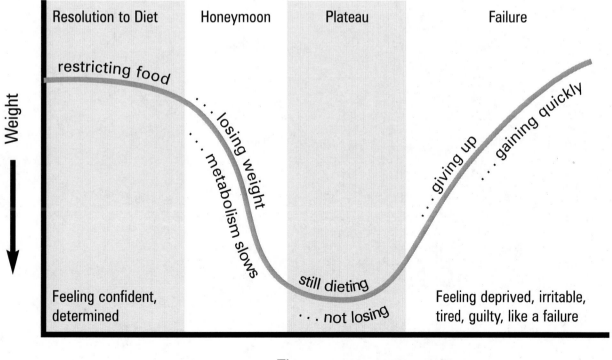

# I KNEW THAT I COULD BLAME MY FAMILY

Of course, our families have some role in how our bodies function. Our genetics help to determine the speed of our metabolism and our body shape. We are all different breeds. "Savannah's Story" helps illustrate this point.

# SAVANNAH'S STORY

One Saturday morning, Star looked in the mirror. Star is a big, beautiful Great Dane. She has long legs and strong muscles, is athletic, and is quite fun. But, Star looked in the mirror and saw a dog that was too big, too fat, and had an ugly coat. She was sad. She started feeling bad about herself when she began watching television and reading fashion magazines. None of the dogs on television looked like her. All the dogs on the television programs and in the fashion magazines were Chihuahuas. They all looked glamorous in beautiful outfits and diamond collars. They went to the coolest dog parks in the world and their owners always seemed to give them lots of attention. Star felt that if she could lose enough weight to be as small as the Chihuahuas on television, she too could have the diamond collar, beautiful clothes, great dog park vacations, and unlimited love.

On the other side of town, Jane also was looking in the mirror. Jane is a Chihuahua like the ones on television and in the magazines. She and Star are great friends. She has the diamond collar and beautiful clothes, but she is still unhappy. She does not like herself very much. She feels like her family buys her fancy clothes to hide the fact that she does not have long, flowing hair like her friend, Savannah. Savannah is a Maltese and has long, pretty white hair. Her family brushes her all the time and puts pretty bows in her hair. Jane feels that others pay Savannah more attention because she has that long, pretty hair. Jane thinks her life would be better if she could get hair extensions. She thinks that when she gets hair extensions, others will find her beautiful and want to play with her more.

Savannah, the Maltese, is quite happy. She does not watch the television shows about the "perfect" size, "perfect" hair, "perfect" clothes, "perfect" vacation, "perfect" family, or "perfect" friends. She knows that her family loves her, and she enjoys just being herself. Sure, sometimes things are hard for her, too. Her legs are very short, and her long hair makes her hot and often gets tangled. Her family does not make an issue of the things about herself that she finds challenging. Instead, they find ways to make her feel special. They take her for walks, play with her, and give her special treats. Savannah also has decided not to get upset. Instead, she chooses to focus on how great her family is and how much she loves them. She also feels lucky to have great friends. Her best friends are Star and Jane.

Savannah is excited to see her friends Star and Jane in the park for their Sunday play date. When Savannah saw Star and Jane lying sadly in the park, she playfully jumped on them and asked what was wrong. Star said that she was hungry. She was on a diet so that she could just get a little smaller and her family would then buy her a beautiful collar and coat. She said, "My family just doesn't like to pay attention to such a big dog." Jane piped up and said, "I know, I just want longer hair because my family would then be happier, like me more, and pet me more. I just can't stand my short hair." Savannah looked at her friends and said, "Star, you are so strong, athletic, fun, and a great listener. Jane, you are so funny, you speak English and Spanish, and you are great at snuggling. I wish that you two would focus on what is great about you rather than what the television and magazines tell you is popular. I miss the beauty that comes from you two accepting yourselves. And, besides, who really decides what is beautiful? Beautiful is not about a shape, a size, a color, a hairstyle, or your clothes. If there is one thing that I do know, it is that beauty lies in finding happiness inside yourself and sharing it with others. We all have our own different ways of bringing happiness to others, and it is unfair to yourself and the world not to be who you really are."

Star struggled, but stopped watching the television shows and reading the magazines that showed that being smaller and having nice stuff would make her happy. She paid attention to what she did well and soon found herself having fun again. She started smiling again when she realized she was strong, a good runner, and had great friends. Jane realized that she had been the only one thinking that she was not beautiful. She allowed herself to know that she did not need long hair to be loved and for others to find her beautiful. Her soul began smiling again. And, when their souls smiled again, they brought happiness to their friends and family who spread happiness to their friends and family who spread happiness to their friends and family until it spread to you today.

Look inside yourself to find what makes you special and beautiful. Be proud of who you are. Let your soul smile. Then you too will bring happiness to your friends and family who make up our world. We are all from different backgrounds and are different "breeds." Embrace your history and who you are.

My culture is: _____

_____

_____

_____

_____

I am proud of my culture because: _____

_____

_____

_____

_____

_____

I celebrate my culture by: _____

_____

_____

_____

_____

_____

# PORTION CONTROL

## LIFESTYLE CHOICES

Our families not only affect the speed of our metabolism but also have helped give us ingrained patterns of behavior. Humans have been proven to be creatures of habit. For most of us, our favorite foods were determined in our childhood and reinforced throughout our entire life. I have a 100% true-blooded Italian friend. I'll bet you'll never guess what her first food choice would be. If you guessed Italian, give yourself a pat on the back. How about my friend whose parents emigrated from Mexico? Mexican food? Boy, you really are smart! We choose to eat what we know and prefer from the start. I have to admit, I have watched segments of my family that I would argue emigrated from the land of convenience. Guess what their favorite foods are? Anything that can come from a drive through. And, let me just say, I prefer convenience myself, but as you may have heard, the foods that are convenient are unfortunately not very nutritious. Sure, they take away the hunger pains, but they do not help our bodies function at top capacity. The interesting thing about convenience food is that, after eating it, our bodies still will crave the nutrients they need, and we often will get hungry again more quickly. Thanks, Mom. Now my taste buds and my brain prefer all this food that is not good for me. Then, when I try to make better choices, I feel like I am depriving myself of what I truly prefer. This cycle begins to create the negative weight that we are battling in this workbook.

## DID YOUR FAMILY TEACH YOU PORTION CONTROL?

Our families are also our guides to teaching us portion control. I have to admit that when I came to the enlightenment of what actual portion sizes are supposed to be, I was shocked. There were also lots of ounces and grams to remember. My problem is that I just cannot bring myself to carry around a scale and weigh everything everywhere I go. Who knows, maybe Fendi will make a cute scale and it will be the next hot accessory that people simply cannot live without. Until then, I'll let you in on another secret—you almost always can eyeball what a normal portion size is.

So, let's begin with fruits and salads. I love them. And they often satisfy a sweet tooth. One serving size of fruit is about the size of a baseball. If you are having fresh cut fruit, ½ cup is about the size of half a baseball. 1 cup of salad is also about the size of a baseball. Hey, why carry a scale when you can look sporty carrying around the baseball?

You may get a chuckle out of the normal meat portion size. A normal meat portion is 3 ounces, which translates to about the size of a deck of cards. Next time you go out to a restaurant, take a look at the portion size set before you. It is almost certainly bigger than the size of a deck of cards. If you prefer fish, the portion is to be 3 ounces as well and measures out to about the size of your checkbook. For those of you who prefer peanut butter for your protein, 2 tablespoons is the normal serving, and that is about the size of a ping pong ball.

How about your dairy and cheese? A normal portion of cheese is 1.5 ounces (two pieces of cheese). For grains, a normal portion of cereal is about one cup, which equals out to about the size of your fist. One pancake the size of a compact disc is a desirable portion, and one piece of bread about the size of a cassette tape is considered a desirable serving size. (Okay, if you have never seen a cassette tape, ask your parents about this reference and they are going to feel really old. Hey, getting old is a whole book unto itself, but I can sum it up in one thought, "I would rather be old, because consider the alternative.")

# I'LL HAVE A SECOND HELPING . . . OF GUILT

Family messages also help determine whether or not we learned to listen to our physical signs of hunger and fullness. Most of us did not grow up in a family that allowed us to determine what time we wanted to eat but instead were told when we would eat according to our parents' schedules rather than our internal cues. That is a casualty of society to which most of us simply have adjusted. Our families also help us determine emotional attachments to food. Have you realized that you might have some guilt attachments to not cleaning off your plate? I was taught that there were starving children in other countries that needed the food that I did not eat. I felt guilty and forced myself to finish the food. After years of this practice, I was very far removed from listening to my body's physical signs of fullness. The rule in my head had become that if I did not want to feel guilt, then I must clean my plate. I gained other emotional attachments to food that remain today. Maybe you can relate. Were you in a family that made you sit at the table and finish everything on your plate before you could leave the table? Me, too. I am not kidding you when I tell you that I still will not eat broccoli. Many an evening was spent in fierce control battles over what would happen to that broccoli on my plate. As I became an obstinate teen, I would get an envelope and offer to send it to those starving children. I did not need any more guilt and did not want to spend my evening at the kitchen table. My parents never let that fly, even though I insisted that I was helping solve world hunger problems. Those messages are still alive and well within me today. Eating for me was not a survival experience; it was a guilt-ridden, control issue. I now realize my food choices were focused on being convenient and tasting great. I had no idea that the broccoli that I was refusing to eat because I did not prefer the taste would be affecting my body. If I had not been trying to express my independence then, I probably would not have to take iron pills now. My choices were affecting my sleep, concentration, mood, energy, self-esteem, and overall well-being.

# UNSPOKEN RULES

**M**essages learned in our families develop into the "rules" of our adulthood. Were you taught any of these rules, or did you have any of these experiences?

- You were taught to feel guilty if you didn't clean your plate.

- One parent always was worried about his/her own weight.

- Family expectations were set very high. You often felt like nothing you did was good enough.

- Your parents placed very high importance on your appearance.

- Family members teased one another about their weight and/or appearance.

- Family members were critical of one another.

- Your parents always made decisions for you and held very tight reins on your independence, or on the other extreme, your family played little to no part in helping their children learn to make good choices.

- You grew up in a family that had poor communication skills.

- Your family did not teach you to recognize, name, and/or manage your emotions.

- Boundaries in your family were unclear. For example, your mom read your diary.

- Dieting was seen as a way to increase self-esteem.

- Family members were poor role models for anger.

My family messages were: _____
_____
_____
_____
_____


The messages I want for a healthy body are: _____
_____
_____
_____
_____

# DO I HAVE A HEALTHY FAMILY?

## HOW DO I DEFINE A HEALTHY FAMILY?

So, what is the definition of a healthy family? According to Joyce Nash in *Binge No More* (1999, Oakland, CA: New Harbinger Publications),

> a healthy, functional family encourages a positive and confident self-concept in children, and parents teach children to understand the language of emotions. Well functioning families encourage all members to express their feelings, thoughts, desires and fantasies while respecting the rights and boundaries of others. Communication between family members is clear, direct, honest, supportive and respectful. Each family member takes responsibility for acknowledging and helping to resolve problems. Differences are worked out through negotiation, and compromises are reached. Rules are flexible and fair. The atmosphere is open and spontaneous. Mistakes are forgiven and viewed as learning tools. All members of the family are encouraged to explore and express their uniqueness and pursue their path in life. Anxiety is low. Trust is high. (p. 72)

## DO I HAVE A HEALTHY FAMILY?

Put a checkmark next to all of the following that apply to you:

_____ In my opinion, my family encourages a positive and confident self-concept in me.

_____ My parents/guardians explain emotions to me.

_____ I am encouraged in my family to express my thoughts.

_____ I am encouraged in my family to express my feelings.

_____ I am encouraged in my family to express my desires.

_____ I am encouraged in my family to express my dreams.

_____ I am encouraged in my family to express my fantasies.

_____ My family respects my privacy.

_____ My family discusses limits and boundaries.

_____ Communication in my family is clear.

_____ Communication in my family is direct.

_____ Communication in my family is honest.

_____ Communication in my family is supportive.

_____ Communication in my family is respectful.

_____ Each family member takes responsibility for his/her mistakes.

_____ Family members feel comfortable discussing problems.

_____ Family members are able to offer suggestions to help others solve problems.

_____ Problems in the family are worked out through negotiation.

_____ Problems in the family are worked out through compromises.

_____ I know what the rules of my family are.

_____ The rules of my family are flexible.

_____ The rules of my family are clear.

_____ I feel free to say or do anything in my house.

_____ I feel free to be myself when I am with my family.

_____ I know that it is okay to make mistakes.

_____ I learn from my mistakes.

_____ My family forgives me if I make a mistake.

_____ I believe that we all can learn from making mistakes.

_____ I am comfortable trying new things around my family.

_____ I trust all my family members.

_____ I am unique.

_____ My family likes that I am unique.

_____ I trust my family.

_____ I do not feel anxious around my family.

The statements that you checked are to be celebrated, enjoyed, and built upon. Statements that you did not check can be goals for your family to work on together.

The goals for my family are: _____

_____

_____

_____

_____

My goals will be:  _____

_____

_____

_____

_____

# IS IT AN EATING DISORDER? WHAT NOW?

PART

2

# HOW DO YOU KNOW WHEN THINGS HAVE GONE TOO FAR?

Recently, I was chatting with a woman while waiting for a plane when a young woman crossed in front of us. The woman with whom I was chatting said, "Wow, she has a body to die for!" The young woman she was referring to was very attractive, but the wording of this woman's statement left me feeling uneasy. I must have frowned because the woman rolled her eyes and stated, "Apparently, you don't agree." I apologized for my reaction and explained that I was traveling on business to do educational seminars on eating disorders. I went on to express my troubled feelings regarding how even in our language the importance of outward appearance has led us to lay our very lives on the line.

I shared with the woman how her statement reminded me of a statistic I recently read from the National Institutes of Health (NIH). The NIH reported that the number one leading cause of death among females age 15 to 24 is complications resulting from anorexia and/or bulimia. I shared a short list of medical complications to include: malnutrition, dehydration, electrolyte imbalances, acid reflux, anemia, dental and gum problems, kidney problems, possible brain shrinkage, heart problems, sleep problems, stunted growth in adolescents, osteoporosis, infertility, and death. The woman stated, "That is the short list? You know, I see famous faces all the time who say they have eating disorders, and I had no idea that the list of medical complications from anorexia and bulimia was so extensive. After all the media attention to this problem, it should be easy to recognize people with these warning signs, right?"

I replied, "It seems that way, but in America's image obsessed culture, it has become increasingly difficult to identify and treat eating disorders in their early stages when treatment can be most effective. Eating disorders often are not even recognized until behavioral patterns have become entrenched and resistance to change has become very high. In the meantime, the ages of people identified in the onset of an eating disorder are getting younger, and those affected by the negative and deadly consequences are increasing every year."

"So, what are the warning signs of an eating disorder?" the woman inquired.

"Well, there are a lot of things to watch out for that most might not think about. Weight, food, calories, dieting, and cooking become the number one topic of conversation and a preoccupation for the person. You may notice the person beginning to skip meals, taking smaller portions, and trying to find a reason not to be hungry. You also may notice that the person is becoming disgusted with certain foods, is unable to accept a compliment, and no matter what size the person truly is will believe he/she is "too fat."

The woman I was chatting with grabbed my arm and said, "You have got to be kidding—that is me!" We discussed how so many of us have been caught in a scary path of unattainable perfection and are missing what true beauty lies within each and every one of us. I continued to share the warning signs of poor nutrition—lightheadedness, dizziness, headaches, sleep problems, frequent sore throats, complaints of feeling cold all the time, erratic menstrual cycles, bad breath, and poor complexion. I shared a simple assessment used where if someone answers "yes" two or more times, I would recommend the person speak with a professional. The questions include the following:

- Do you worry you have lost control over how much you eat?

- Have you recently lost more than 15 pounds in a three-month period?

- Do you believe yourself to be fat when others say you are too thin?

- Would you say that food dominates your life?

- Do you make yourself sick because you feel uncomfortably full?

The woman then put out her hand to me and said, "Before I let you know this, I want to let you know my name is Susie." She whispered, "I answered "yes" to three of those questions but never thought of myself as having an eating disorder. I thought they were just people who looked like skeletons."

I shared the definitions of medically recognized eating disorders. Anorexia Nervosa is a condition of someone who is 15% or more underweight, who has an intense fear of gaining weight even though he/she is underweight, and denies the seriousness of the low body weight. Bulimia Nervosa is recurrent episodes of binge eating. Binge eating is defined as eating more food than most under similar circumstances, with a sense of lack of control over eating during the episode. People with bulimia then will use any number of ways to take out the food that they just put into their bodies, the most common of those methods being "purging," more commonly called "throwing up." I then shared the diagnosis that is coming to the forefront in modern society—Binge Eating Disorder, which is binging without trying to get rid of the food that has been eaten.

Susie bravely began to share her private story of her own body image issues, constant dieting, poor self-esteem, emotional attachments with food, and her embarrassment about her issues. I shared of the courage necessary to admit there is a problem. Once someone has progressed into being able to be diagnosed with an eating disorder, a treatment team of individuals is necessary to monitor and promote progress. Typically, a therapist, psychiatrist, medical doctor, and nutritionist are necessary to deal with the medical and emotional complications that arise from the disorder. Most importantly, I shared that it would be important that all of these specialties have experience in helping someone with an eating disorder. Susie admitted that she could not believe she had shared this secret with a total stranger but admitted that she would be scared to death to talk with a therapist. I shared how I can understand that her discussions would be difficult but that she can find a comfort level with someone who can help her enjoy being in her own skin.

Susie stated, "I really don't have the time or the money for that." I challenged her to think of how many times a day she worried about her weight, dieting, and disliking her body. Susie stated, "A whole heck of a lot." I then challenged her to think about what she can do when she is not worrying about her weight, dieting, and disliking her body. Susie's eyes lit up and stated, "I will finally get to go on that cruise I have been dreaming of!" I reminded Susie of the amount of money that she has spent on diets and other cosmetic products that she felt could make a "quick fix" and failed her. Susie laughed and said, "You are right; there is the money for my cruise!" We talked about what it meant to be healthy versus looking like someone she is not and how focusing on the wonderful things about her can fill her back up with enough love and energy to last a lifetime. Susie smiled and said, "More than a lifetime, honey; when I learn to quit obsessing about my body and learn how to focus on the gifts within me, the first thing I am going to do is teach my daughter and granddaughters. That will be my motivation, and that gift of knowledge will last long after my lifetime." Susie and I then had to board the plane. We found our seats and enjoyed our safe flight. About one year later, I received an e-mail from Susie. It was a short, simple note: "Thanks for helping me on my journey to finding the great gifts in me. I found someone to help me with my body image and self-esteem. I rewarded myself and just came back from my first cruise to the Bahamas. It was fantastic!"

# WARNING SIGNS OF AN EATING DISORDER

As in Susie's story, ethics and values that promote eating disorders often are embedded in our very culture. A more comprehensive list of warning signs to eating disorders is listed below. This worksheet is intended to be used by everyone . . . in middle and high school health classes, at local gyms, or anywhere these signs could be addressed. It also is meant to be used as part of finding out where you are now in your life. This worksheet also can be used for someone you are concerned about. It is important to remember that the most successful time to treat someone with an eating disorder is before it can be clinically diagnosed as an eating disorder. Let's work together to recognize problem patterns before they become more harmful.

Please put a check by all that apply:

____ Are you finding excuses to eat when you are not physically hungry?

____ Are you always trying to find a reason not to be hungry?

____ Do you find yourself disgusted with certain foods?

____ Are you constantly trying to convince others that you are really healthy?

____ Do you visit websites that promote weight loss?

____ Are you often reading books about weight loss?

____ Have you ever felt guilt after eating?

____ Have your tried every diet?

____ Do you spend the majority of your time talking about food and weight?

____ Are you embarrassed to eat in front of other people?

____ Do you feel that people are judging what you choose to eat?

____ Do you spend more than 25% of your day thinking about weight, food, cooking, dieting, and your shape?

____ Do you find yourself preoccupied with weight?

____ Do you find yourself constantly thinking about food?

____ Are you often in the process of a diet? (Starting, ending, or searching for a new one?)

____ Do you obsess over food labels?

____ Are you finding excuses to skips meals?

____ If you eat outside of your diet, have you ever vomited to get rid of the calories?

____ If you eat outside of your diet, have you ever used laxatives to get rid of the calories?

____ If you eat outside of your diet, have you ever used diet pills, water pills, or "natural" products to get rid of the calories?

____ Have you ever made self-defeating statements after eating? ("I am so fat," "I am so ugly," etc.)

____ Do you find yourself eating large amounts of food inconsistent with your weight?

____ Have you ever hidden food from others?

____ Have you ever stolen food from others?

____ Have you ever binged on food?

____ Do you play with food to make others think that you ate (shift food around on the plate to look eaten, cut food into tiny pieces but not eat it, etc.)?

____ Do you ever chew food and spit it out or drop food into a napkin on your lap to later throw away?

____ Do you eat food in rigid sequence? ( e.g., "I have to have protein before carbohydrates.")

____ Do you feel like foods cannot touch each other?

____ Do you eat a very limited variety of foods?

____ Do you hide food in strange places (e.g., closets, cabinets, suitcases, under the bed) to avoid eating (Anorexia) or to eat at a later time (Bulimia and Binge Eating)?

____ Have you ever flushed uneaten food down the toilet?

____ Do you alternate between periods of restrictive dieting and overeating, sometimes accompanied by dramatic weight gain or loss?

____ Have you ever fainted, and it was not explained by another medical problem?

____ Do you often feel lightheaded or dizzy, not explained by any other medical problem?

_____ Do you often get headaches?

_____ Have you been experiencing constipation or incontinence?

_____ Do you often have frequent sore throats and/or swollen glands?

_____ Do you often complain of feeling cold?

_____ Are you starting to lose hair?

_____ Does your complexion look pale or "grey"?

_____ Are you beginning to notice more hair on your face and arms?

_____ Have you noticed swelling on your cheeks near your ears (caused by inflammation of the saliva glands)?

_____ Has your menstrual cycle stopped or become erratic?

_____ Have you noticed unusual redness and/or puffiness around the eyes?

_____ Have you noticed bad breath, dry mouth, and/or cracked lips, caused by purging and dehydration?

_____ Have your sleeping patterns changed?

_____ Has your blood pressure changed?

_____ Do you notice that you are always checking yourself out in the mirror?

_____ Do you have body parts that you have begun to "hate" or that "make you sick"?

_____ Do you have difficulty shopping for clothing?

_____ Do you get upset over clothing size changes?

_____ Have you begun to wear baggy or layered clothing in attempts to hide "the fat" or to help keep you warm?

_____ Do you have trouble paying attention and/or concentrating?

_____ Do you feel that there are "good" and "bad" foods?

_____ Do you have a shorter temper than in the past?

_____ Are you more argumentative than before?

_____ Have you become more private with your feelings?

_____ Have you begun to isolate yourself from friends and activities because of weight and shape concerns?

_____ Do you continue to feel anxiety about being fat even after you have lost weight?

____ Do you continue to complain about being fat in spite of normal or thin appearance?

____ Do you define your self-worth with your weight?

____ Do you feel like you have low self-esteem?

____ Do you feel worthless?

____ Do you often put yourself down and complain of being "too stupid" or "too fat"?

____ Do you like everything to be "perfect"?

____ Do you feel like you exercise too often?

____ Do you continue to exercise despite fatigue, illness, injury, or bad weather?

____ Have you ever binged?

____ Have you ever purged?

____ Have you ever refused to eat?

____ Have you used diet pills, laxatives, drugs, or any other supplement to try to lose weight?

____ I worry about not being able to control eating, and while eating, not being able to stop.

____ I prefer to eat alone.

____ I am a chronic dieter; I have tried the majority of diet plans.

____ My life would be better if I would lose weight.

____ I have hidden food in strange places (closets, cabinets, suitcases, under the bed) to eat at a later time.

____ I have vague or secretive eating patterns.

____ I blame my failure in social and professional communities on weight.

____ I feel that food is my only friend.

____ I am frequently out of breath after relatively light activities.

____ I have excessive sweating and shortness of breath.

____ I have high blood pressure and/or cholesterol.

____ I have leg and joint pain.

____ I have continued to gain weight.

____ It is harder to get around since I gained weight.

____ I have had a loss of sexual desire.

____ I have been experiencing mood swings.

____ I feel depressed.

____ I feel anxious.

The scary part about this worksheet is that almost no one walks away without checking something on the list. If you checked more than five, please seek professional help.

# HOW CAN I TELL IF SOMEONE HAS AN EATING DISORDER?

Even though there are many commonalities among people living with an eating disorder, it is also important to remember the following:

- A person can be any size and have an eating disorder.
- Their ages span from preadolescence through old age.
- They represent every social and economic level of society.
- They come from different cultures and different races of people.
- Some are very underweight and some are very overweight.
- Eating disorders are real medical illnesses that need to receive treatment

Use the following "Questions for Assessment." Be honest.

# QUESTIONS FOR ASSESSMENT

Do you worry you have lost control over how much you eat?

Have you recently lost more than 15 pounds in a three-month period?

Do you believe yourself to be fat when others say you are too thin?

Would you say that food dominates your life?

Do you make yourself sick because you feel uncomfortably full?

If you answer "yes" to one or more of these questions, please seek professional help immediately.

# HOW MANY PEOPLE ARE STRUGGLING?

Just an author's note—it is truly difficult to determine actual statistics for people struggling with an eating disorder. Currently, physicians do not have to report the exact incidence of eating disorders as part of their standard protocol. So, even if someone tells a doctor that he/she has been restricting eating and often purging what he/she does eat, there is not a requirement to report this data. Even in settings where there is a requirement, it is very difficult to recognize someone struggling with an eating disorder until he/she is actually in a medical crisis. People struggling with an eating disorder are very secretive about the process and also report being quite embarrassed by their behavior. There are very few incidents of people struggling with an eating disorder walking into their doctor's office and sharing all the behaviors they are currently experiencing. So, currently the only reliable statistics available are from those brave souls that have attended a treatment program and agreed to participate in studies.

Current statistics for those struggling with eating disorders in the United States according to the National Institute for Mental Health (NIMH) are as follows:

- Most studies report 1% of women struggle with diagnosis of anorexia, but the NIMH current report is up to 3.7%.

- 95% of people struggling with anorexia are women.

- Age of onset of anorexia is normally between 11 to 22.

- Anorexia is the deadliest mental health disorder. 15 % of the more than 1 million Americans with anorexia will die from it.

- Estimates for the occurrence of Bulimia Nervosa range between 1% to 4% of the population.

- Although eating disorders can affect people of all ages, 86% of individuals afflicted with these disorders report onset before the age of 20. The occurrence of eating disorders among college age women can be considered almost epidemic.

- Between 19% and 30% of college age women display bulimic behavior.

# ANOREXIA CASE STUDY

Hi. My name is Susie, and I am in recovery for anorexia and for being a beauty queen. Being labeled as a beauty can be both a blessing and a curse. I figured out young that I got a lot of attention, admiration, and acceptance mainly for my looks. Everywhere I went, people complimented me on my appearance. It seemed to please my parents so much, and they put me into pageants starting at age 4. By the time I was 10, my room was filled with ribbons and trophies, and my self-worth had become intertwined with my appearance. As I came into puberty, however, my body began to change. Before I went through my initial growth spurt, I had gained 30 pounds. I did not understand that this was normal for my body and that it was part of growing up. Instead, everyone commented on my weight gain, and I began to eat less. Eventually, I grew 4 inches and was skinnier than ever, which in turn gave me attention again from all those around me commenting on how thin I was and how jealous they were. I think that was it—the moment that I decided that my weight determined my status and how much (or little) people would like me. As I got into high school, I realized that I could continue to get even more attention through guys. By the time I hit 19, I had passed tests without having to take them ("she's just so cute"), received jewelry, clothes, trips, and even a car as a direct result of my beauty. Heck, with the presents that were in my high school years and beyond, there was no way I would allow myself to become "fat and ordinary." Then the day came when I was walking into the grocery store and collapsed. After entering the hospital at 5'9" and 100 pounds, I was admitted with low potassium and cardiac arrhythmias. I remember the doctor explaining anorexia to me and all the while thinking he was just jealous. Maybe his wife was fat or something. I did not have a problem; he did. The more the staff tried to help me, the more flaws I would find in them and then rationalize that they did not understand what it was like to be beautiful. I also remember that when they discussed feeding me, I had to be given tranquilizers because I was freaking out. Didn't they understand that is what I am—beautiful and skinny—there is nothing else. If they take that away, I am nothing.

# THE CLINICAL DIAGNOSIS

So, how do clinicians diagnose Anorexia? Clinicians use a book called the Diagnostic & Statistical Manual of Mental Disorders, Fourth Edition (DSM-IV) (American Psychological Association, 1994). This manual provides step-by-step definitions that professionals use to diagnose. The DSM-IV lists the following as diagnostic criteria for Anorexia Nervosa:

A.    Refusal to maintain body weight at or above a minimally normal weight for age and height (e.g., weight loss leading to a maintenance of body weight less than 85% of that expected, or failure to make expected weight gain during period of growth, leading to body weight less than 85% of that expected).

B. Intense fear of gaining weight or becoming fat, even though underweight.

C. Disturbance in the way in which one's body weight or shape is experienced, undue influence of body weight or shape on self-evaluation, or denial of the seriousness of the current low body weight.

D. In postmenarcheal females, amenorrhea (i.e., the absence of at least three consecutive menstrual cycles). (A woman is considered to have amenorrhea if her periods occur only following hormone, e.g., estrogen, administration.)

Specify type:

- Restricting Type: during the current episode of Anorexia Nervosa, the person has not regularly engaged in binge-eating or purging behavior (i.e., self-induced vomiting or the misuse of laxatives, diuretics or enemas)

- Binge Eating/Purging Type: during the current episode of Anorexia Nervosa, the person has regularly engaged in binge eating or purging behavior (i.e., self-induced vomiting or the misuse of laxatives, diuretics or enemas)

The DSM-IV lists the following as diagnostic criteria for Bulimia Nervosa:

A. Recurrent episodes of binge eating. An episode of binge eating is characterized by both of the following:

(1) eating, in a discrete period of time (e.g., within any 2-hour period), an amount of food that is definitely larger than most people would eat during a similar period of time and under similar circumstances

(2) a sense of lack of control over eating during the episode (e.g., a feeling that one cannot stop eating or control what or how much one is eating)

B. Recurrent inappropriate compensatory behavior in order to prevent weight gain, such as self-induced vomiting; misuse of laxatives, diuretics, enemas, or other medications; fasting; or excessive exercise.

C. The binge eating and inappropriate compensatory behaviors both occur, on average, at least twice a week for 3 months.

D. Self-evaluation is unduly influenced by body shape and weight.

E. The disturbance does not occur exclusively during episodes of Anorexia Nervosa.

Specify type:

- Purging Type: during the current episode of Bulimia Nervosa, the person has regularly engaged in self-induced vomiting or the misuse of laxatives, diuretics, or enemas

- Nonpurging Type: during the current episode of Bulimia Nervosa, the person has used other inappropriate compensatory behaviors, such as fasting or excessive exercise, but has not regularly engaged in self-induced vomiting or the misuse of laxatives, diuretics, or enemas

# BINGE EATING DISORDER CASE STUDY

Michael's story is shared after his losing battle with binge eating. Mike grew up the oldest of three siblings. Mike's younger brother, Dave, was always made out to be the star child. He was rewarded for playing sports and charming the girls. His sister, May, was the second favored child. She was rewarded for being the girl and the youngest in the family. The only attention that Mike received came as a result of his role of being the oldest. In his family, that seemed to translate into being the responsible member of the family. He could avoid getting into trouble by keeping up on the household chores and sacrificing for his siblings.

Mike came to learn in therapy, however, that his sacrifices were actually a result of emotional abuse. A good example of a "sacrifice" that Mike would make occurred during the holiday season. Growing up in a Catholic household, Mike and his family would celebrate Christmas. One Christmas morning, Mike woke up and walked out to the living room where the Christmas tree and presents were. In the early morning light, Mike's eyes lit up with delight. There in the living room sat a brand new red bike that he had asked for on numerous occasions. You see, Mike was an introverted kid. His introverted nature was part biological, but felt more like necessity than anything. Mike learned to keep his desires to himself. Any time that Mike shared his true desires, he learned that they did not matter. It hurt Mike when his family, whom he was supposed to trust the most, would make fun of his needs or just ignore them. Even though Mike's family hurt him when he expressed his desires, he still kept asking for a bike. He would often sit in the picture window and watch his little brother, Dave, play with all the other neighborhood kids. Mike fantasized about being outside playing with them and making friends. He had longed for this opportunity for so long, and he had shared this desire with his parents on several occasions. Standing there in his pajamas on Christmas morning, he felt that warm feeling that comes from feeling heard and accepted. He felt his eyes fill up with tears of happiness. What a wonderful moment for him. He stated that it felt surreal, even like it was all happening in slow motion. He was glad of that, because he never wanted this feeling to end.

Then Dave came running out and literally pushed Mike out of the way. What a metaphor for how Mike felt in his family. He had been invisible, but now things were going to change. His family recognized him, and the bike was a tangible token of his value and importance in the family. Unfortunately, this surreal happiness quickly turned to the detachment of shock. After Dave pushed Mike out of the way, Dave squealed with delight to see the new bike he had asked for. You see, Dave had asked for a new bike as well. Dave's blue bike was still in good shape, and Mike stood in shock insisting that the bike had to be his new bike. Mike remembered hearing himself protest that the shiny red bike was his. Dave grabbed the card off the bike and read aloud, "To a great son, Dave. Love, Mom and Dad."

Mike looked around frantically; where was the bike he had asked for? There was a strawberry shortcake bike under the tree as well, but that was clearly for his sister, May. Mike felt himself fall to his knees and felt the tears of happiness change to tears of sadness. How could this be? He was a good son, too. He did all the chores in the house from cleaning the toilets, to cleaning the gutters, to keeping up with the pool. He got straight As in school. He always stayed out of their way. If he wasn't doing the chores, he was hiding away in his room reading. It kept him safe from their verbally abusive words and criticisms. What was it that he did wrong? The next thing he knew, his parents were sitting in their traditional places on the couch giving the go ahead to open presents. It was then that Mike saw the stack of IOUs that he also had received during Easter, his birthday, and any other time that his brother and sister received presents. His parents had explained to him the necessity of budgeting years ago and the importance of giving instead of receiving. Mike's holiday presents that year were an IOU for one game, an IOU for one trip to the movie, and an IOU for one bike.

Mike knew better than to protest verbally and came to figure out during talk therapy that his binging began as part of his way of "stuffing" his feelings, namely anger and sadness, and "filling up" with love. Hey, it worked. Large amounts of chocolate really did stimulate the same chemicals in the brain as the feeling of love. Mike endured ongoing emotional and often physical abuse until he moved on to go into the military, got married, and had children. Even though he was away from the abuse of his parents, the coping skill and defense mechanism of turning to food to stuff emotions to feel better never went away. Mike demonstrated the courage to begin his battle with the demons of his past by entering into talk therapy. He had carried into adulthood the childhood messages of self-sacrifice and self discipline. He began to learn the skills to battle the negative weight and to label, monitor, and channel his emotions in a positive way. He was at the cusp of celebrating surviving the challenging life he had endured by taking his first romantic cruise with his wife. The day before he was to leave for the cruise, he lost his battle to a massive heart attack at age 53. His story remains as an ongoing learning tool for education about the devastating effects of emotional abuse and the value of learning to choose positive outlets for managing our emotions.

# THE CLINICAL DIAGNOSIS

The preliminary diagnostic criteria for binge eating are as follows:

A.  Recurrent episodes of binge eating. An episode of binge eating is characterized by both of the following:

(1)  eating, in a discrete period of time (e.g., within any 2-hour period), an amount of food that is definitely larger than most people would eat in a similar period of time under similar circumstances

(2)  a sense of lack of control over eating during the episode (e.g., a feeling that one cannot stop eating or control what or how much one is eating)

B.  The binge eating episodes are associated with at least three of the following:

(1)  eating much more rapidly than normal

(2)  eating until feeling uncomfortably full

(3)  eating large amounts of food when not feeling physically hungry

(4)  eating alone because of being embarrassed by how much one is eating

(5)  feeling disgusted with oneself, depressed, or feeling very guilty after overeating

C.  Marked distress regarding binge eating.

D.  The binge eating occurs, on average, at least 2 days a week for 6 months.

E.  The binge eating is not associated with the regular use of inappropriate compensatory behaviors (e.g., purging, fasting, excessive exercise) and does not occur exclusively during the course of anorexia nervosa or bulimia nervosa.

# REASONS WHY BINGES OCCUR

Ongoing research suggests several different reasons that binges occur:

- Binges can be seen as a reward in and of themselves and a way to cope with daily stresses and feelings.

- The types of food vary but are often sweet and/or high in fat content.

- During a binge, people may eat an astounding amount of food in a short time. They may consume thousands and thousands of calories in soft foods that are high in sugars and carbohydrates.

- People often eat so quickly that they may not bother to chew. Instead, they may gulp down the food without even tasting it.

- Binges often end only when people are interrupted by another person, they fall asleep, or their stomachs hurt from over-extension.

- Some binges are planned in advance, but generally they are impulsive.

- Binging may temporarily numb negative feelings, but this state is quickly followed by feelings of failure.

- People often are ashamed of their binges and view the behavior as a loss of control and a reason for low self-esteem.

- Constant dieting and restricting food becomes a way of life for the compulsive overeater.

# CONSEQUENCES OF BINGING BEHAVIOR

People who are obese and also have binge eating disorder are at risk for:

- Diabetes
- High blood pressure
- High blood cholesterol levels
- Gallbladder disease
- Heart disease
- Certain types of cancer
- Obesity
- Arthritis
- Bone deterioration
- Stroke
- Upper respiratory problems
- Skin disorders
- Menstrual irregularities
- Ovarian abnormalities
- Complications of pregnancy
- Depression, anxiety, and other mood disorders
- Suicidal thoughts
- Substance abuse

# WARNING SIGNS FOR BINGE EATING DISORDER

Warning Signs for Binge Eating Disorder are as follows:

- Rapid weight gain or obesity
- Constant weight fluctuations
- Frequently eating an abnormal amount of food in a short period of time (usually less than two hours)
- Does not use methods to purge food
- Eats rapidly (i.e., frequently swallowing without chewing)
- Feeling a lack of control over one's eating (i.e., unable to stop)
- Eating alone, "secretive eating habits," hiding food, etc.
- Eating late at night
- Eating when not hungry
- Disgust and shame with self after overeating
- Hoarding food (especially high calorie / junk food)
- Coping with emotional and psychological states such as stress, unhappiness, or disappointment by eating
- Eating large amounts of food without being hungry
- Consuming food to the point of being uncomfortable or even in pain
- Attributing one's successes and failures to weight
- Avoiding social situations, especially those involving food
- Depressed mood
- Anxious mood

# WHAT HAPPENS WHEN YOUR BODY GETS MAD?

Your body can only take so much before it will get mad at your choices. Your body will kick into survival mode and fight for you to live. You might be thinking from the neck up that it is so "important" to look like a movie star. Your mind might be self-medicating hurt from the latest assault from somebody on your mind, body, or soul. Regardless of the reasons for binge eating, if you continue to make poor nutritional choices, some of the following major medical side effects can occur:

**Malnutrition**—caused by under-eating or overeating

- The word malnutrition indicates deficiency of energy, protein, and micronutrients (e.g., vitamin A, iodine, and iron), either singularly or in combination.

- It can cause severe health risks including (but not limited to) respiratory infections, kidney failure, blindness, heart attack, and death.

**Dehydration**—caused by the depletion or lack of intake of fluids in the body, or by restriction of carbohydrates and fat

- Restriction/starvation, vomiting, and laxative abuse are the primary causes of dehydration in sufferers of eating disorders.

- Symptoms include dizziness, weakness, or darkening of urine. Dehydration can lead to kidney failure, heart failure, seizures, brain damage, and death.

**Electrolyte Imbalances**—Electrolytes are essential to the production of the body's "natural electricity" that ensures healthy teeth, joints and bones, nerve and muscle impulses, kidneys and heart, blood sugar levels, and the delivery of oxygen to the cells.

**Chemistries**—Uric acid elevated; cholesterol is abnormal (elevated or depressed); carotene is elevated; there are deficiencies of trace minerals; blood glucose is low.

**Ketoacidosis**—High levels of acids build up in the blood (known as ketones), caused by the body burning fat (instead of sugar and carbohydrates) to get energy. Ketoacidosis can be a result of starvation, excessive purging, dehydration, hyperglycemia, and/or alcohol abuse (it can also be a result of uncontrolled or untreated diabetes). It can lead to coma and death.

**Iron Deficiency, Anemia**—This makes the oxygen transporting units within the blood useless and can lead to fatigue, shortness of breath, increased infections, and heart palpitations.

**Endocrine**—T-3 deficiency (leading to bradycardia, sluggish reflexes, dry skin, cold intolerance, hypercarotenemia, and various abnormalities of the hair), abnormal calcium levels, and symptoms of hypogonadism

**Impaired Neuromuscular Function**—due to vitamin and mineral deficiencies (specifically potassium), and malnutrition

**Swelling**—in face and cheeks (following self-induced vomiting)

**Callused or Bruised Fingers**—caused by repeated use of fingers to induce vomiting

**Dry Skin and Hair, Brittle Hair and Nails, Hair Loss**—caused by vitamin and mineral deficiencies, malnutrition, and dehydration

**Lanugo** (soft downy hair on face, back, and arms)—caused by a protective mechanism built in to the body to help keep a person warm during periods of starvation and malnutrition, and the hormonal imbalances that result

**Edema** (swelling of the soft tissues as a result of excess water accumulation)—Edema is most common in the legs and feet of binge eaters and in the abdominal area of anorexics and/or bulimics (and can be caused by laxative and diuretic use).

**Muscle Atrophy**—wasting away of muscle and decrease in muscle mass due to the body feeding off of itself

**Hyponatremia** (related to "water-loading")—As stated above, electrolytes are essential to proper body functioning. Drinking too much water (more than eight, 8-ounce glasses in fewer than 12 hours) can cause Hyponatremia (not enough sodium in the blood), especially in someone already malnourished or dehydrated. Hyponatremia can cause fluid in the lungs, the brain to swell, nauseousness, vomiting, confusion, and even death.

**Dental and Mouth**—Increased dental cares; highly sensitive teeth from gingival deterioration; pyorrhea lacerations and contusions of the oral cavity from use of objects to induce emesis; tooth loss; erosion of enamel; altered bite; bleeding gums; oral sensitivity; decalcification of teeth; erosion of tooth enamel; severe decay; gum disease (caused by stomach acids and enzymes from vomiting); vitamin D and calcium deficiencies; and hormonal imbalance. Also, the health of teeth can suffer due to lack of exercise that comes from the process of eating certain foods. Dental problems can sometimes indicate problems with the heart.

**TMJ "Syndrome" and Related TMJ Problems**—TMJ is defined as degenerative arthritis within the tempero-mandibular joint in the jaw (where the lower jaw hinges to the skull) creating pain in the joint area, headaches, and problems chewing and opening/closing the mouth. Vitamin deficiencies and teeth grinding (often related to stress) can both be causes.

**Dermatologic**—dry skin, loss of subcutaneous tissues and fat in general, and scars (such as on knuckles due to inducing emesis)

**Lowered Body Temperature/Temperature Sensitivity**—caused by loss of healthy insulating layer of fat and lowered blood pressure

**Easily Bruising Skin**—Vitamin deficiencies that decrease the body's ability to heal itself, low blood pressure, low platelet count, and/or extreme weight loss all will lead to easily bruised skin that can take a long time to heal.

**Chronic Fatigue Syndrome**—continuous and crippling fatigue related to a weakened immune system

**Hyperactivity**—manic episodes of not being able to sit still

**Ophthalmologic**—transient blurred vision, dark circles, puffiness under the eyes

**Osteoporosis**—thinning of the bones with reduction in bone mass due to depletion of calcium and bone protein, predisposing to fractures

**Osteopenia**—below normal bone mass indicating a calcium and/or vitamin D deficiency leading to osteoporosis. Hormone imbalance/deficiencies associated with the loss of the menstrual cycle also can increase risk of osteoporosis and osteopenia.

**Kidney Infection and Failure**—Kidneys "clean" poisons from the body, regulate acid concentration, and maintain water balance. Vitamin deficiencies, dehydration, infection, and low blood pressure increase the risks of and are associated with kidney infection, thus making permanent kidney damage and kidney failure more likely.

**Effects on Brain and CNS**—lack of REM sleep; affected hypothalamus (lower body temperature, loss of shivering response, cold intolerance, and malfunction of entire temperature regulating system) due to chronic malnutrition; EEG abnormalities; shrinking of the brain

**Cardiovascular**—slow pulse; low blood pressure; electrocardiogram abnormalities; Hypovolemia Myocardiopathy and CHF (especially with use of ipecac as a vomiting inducer)

**High Blood Pressure, Hypertension** (more common in those with binge eating and/or Binge Eating Disorder)—elevated blood pressure exceeding 140 over 90. High blood pressure can cause blood vessel changes in the back of the eye creating vision impairment, abnormal thickening of the heart muscle, kidney failure, and brain damage.

**Low Platelet Count or Thrombocytopenia**—caused by low levels of vitamin B12 and folic acid, and/or by excessive alcohol. It also may be an indication of a suppressed immune system or immune dysfunction.

**Disruptions in Blood Sugar Levels**—Low blood sugar/hypoglycemia can indicate problems with the liver or kidneys and can lead to neurological and mental deterioration.

**Elevated Blood Sugar/Hyperglycemia**—Elevated blood sugar/hyperglycemia can lead to diabetes, liver and kidney shutdown, and circulatory and immune system problems.

**Diabetes**—high blood sugar as a result of low production of insulin. This can be caused by hormonal imbalances, hyperglycemia, or chronic pancreatitis.

**Gastrointestinal**—abdominal pain, bloating, and fullness; esophageal perforations and lacerations (Mallory-Weiss Syndrome); irritable bowel syndrome; ulceration of the bowel; malabsorption of nutrients; exacerbation of hemorrhoids; esophagitis

**Cramps, Bloating, Constipation, Diarrhea, Incontinence**—caused by increased or decreased bowel activity

**Peptic Ulcers**—aggravated or made more severe by increased stomach acids, cigarette smoking, or high consumption of caffeine or alcohol

**Tearing of Esophagus**—caused by self-induced vomiting

**Mallory-Weiss Tear**—a tear of the gastro-esophageal junction associated with vomiting

**Gastric Rupture**—spontaneous stomach erosion, perforation, or rupture

**Barrett's Esophagus**—Associated with cancer of the esophagus and caused by esophageal reflux, this is a change in the cells within the esophagus.

**Digestive Difficulties**—A deficiency in digestive enzymes will lead to the body's inability to properly digest food and absorb nutrients. This can lead to malabsorption problems, malnutrition, and electrolyte imbalances. Related diseases that may be triggered by a history of an eating disorder include Celiac Disease (gluten sensitivity) and Crohn's Disease

**Gastrointestinal Bleeding**—bleeding into the digestive tract

**Esophageal Reflux/Acid Reflux Disorders**—Partially digested items in the stomach, mixed with acid and enzymes, regurgitate back into the esophagus, leading to damage to the esophagus, larynx, and lungs and increasing the chance of development of cancer of the esophagus and voice box. Reflux can become severe enough that food cannot be kept down at all, and medical attention should be sought immediately.

**Cancer**—of the throat and voice box (larynx) due to acid reflux disorders

**Refeeding Syndrome** (related to treatment)—Starved or severely malnourished patients can undergo life-threatening fluid and electrolyte shifts following the initiation of aggressive nutritional support therapies. This phenomenon is known as "refeeding syndrome" and can occur in patients receiving either enteral (tube feeding) or parenteral (intravenous feeding) nutritional support. To avoid the development of refeeding syndrome, nutrition support in patients at risk should be increased slowly while assuring adequate amounts of vitamins and minerals. Organ function, fluid balance, and serum electrolytes (especially phosphorus, potassium, and magnesium) need to be monitored daily during the first week and less often thereafter.

**Menstrual Irregularity or Amenorrhea/Loss of Menstrual Cycle**—due to lack of secreting hormone, estrogen, by the ovaries. Loss of the menstrual cycle also can lead to osteopenia and osteoporosis.

**Polycystic Ovarian Syndrome**—One study has suggested that people with eating disorders are at an increased risk for developing Polycystic Ovarian Syndrome (PCO), and that recovery from the eating disorder should be part of treatment for PCO.

**Loss of Sexual Appetite**

**Breast Atrophy**

**Problems During Pregnancy**—including potential for high risk pregnancies; miscarriage; stillborn babies; death; or chronic illness from minor to severe in children born (all due to malnutrition, dehydration, vitamin, and hormone deficiencies)

**Depression**—Mood swings and depression will be caused by physiological factors such as electrolyte imbalances, hormone and vitamin deficiencies, malnutrition, and dehydration. Living with the eating disorder behaviors themselves will cause depression. Depression also can lead the sufferer back into the cycle of the eating disorder (or may have been the initial problem before the onset of the ED).

**Pancreatitis**—Pancreatitis is when digestive enzymes attack the pancreas. It can be caused by repeated stomach trauma (such as with vomiting), alcohol consumption, or the excessive use of laxatives or diet pills.

**Weakness and Fatigue**—caused by generalized poor eating habits, electrolyte imbalances, vitamin and mineral deficiencies, depression, malnutrition, and heart problems

**Insomnia**—problems falling and/or staying asleep

**Arthritis** (degenerative)—can be caused by hormonal imbalances and vitamin deficiencies as well as increased stress on the joints in individuals who suffer with binge eating

**Liver Failure**—The liver aids in removing waste from cells and aids in digestion; a human being cannot live without the liver. Fasting and taking acetaminophen (drug found in over-the-counter painkillers) increase risks for liver damage and failure. Loss of menstruation and dehydration (putting women at risk for too much iron in their system), and chronic heart failure also can lead to liver damage or failure.

**Bad Circulation, Slowed or Irregular Heartbeat, Arrhythmias, Angina, Heart Attack**—There are many factors associated with having an eating disorder that can lead to heart problems or a heart attack. Sudden cardiac arrest can cause permanent damage to the heart or instant death. Electrolyte imbalances (especially potassium deficiency), dehydration, malnutrition, low blood pressure, extreme orthostatic hypotension, abnormally slow heart rate, electrolyte imbalances, and hormonal imbalances all can lead to serious problems with the heart. High blood pressure, accumulation of fat deposits around the heart muscle, high cholesterol, decreased exercise due to lack of mobility, and diabetes also can lead to serious heart problems.

**Low Blood Pressure/Hypotension** (more common in those with anorexia and/or bulimia)—caused by lowered body temperature, malnutrition, and dehydration. Low blood pressure / hypotension can cause heart arrhythmias, shock, or myocardial infarction.

**Orthostatic Hypotension** (sudden drop in blood pressure upon sitting up or standing)—symptoms include dizziness, blurred vision, passing out, heart pounding, and headaches.

**Pulmonary**—aspiration pneumonia

**Renal**—prerenal and renal azotemia due to diminished renal pertusion and chronic dehydration; tubular and collecting system abnormalities due to electrolyte abnormality; predisposition to renal stones; kidney failure

**Seizures**—The increased risk of seizures in anorexic and bulimic individuals may be caused by dehydration, hyperglycemia, or ketoacidosis. It is also possible that lesions on the brain caused by long-term malnutrition and lack of oxygen-carrying cells to the brain may play a role.

**Miscellaneous**—

- *Bacterial and fungal infections*

- *Bilateral parotid gland swelling*

- *Paralysis*—transient (or temporary) paralysis as shown by extreme weakness of muscles or not being able to move at all. Paralysis is caused by low levels of potassium, and/or the degeneration of nerve cells in the spinal cord or in the brain, which have been deprived of essential nutrients. Left untreated, periods of paralysis may happen more frequently and more severely, lead to permanent muscle weakness, and even result in death.

- *Death* caused by any of the following or any combination of the following: heart attack or heart failure; lung collapse; internal bleeding; stroke; kidney failure; liver failure; pancreatitis; gastric rupture; perforated ulcer; depression; suicide

(Resource: www.somethingfishy.com)

# I LOVE SOMEONE WHO IS STRUGGLING —WHAT CAN I DO?

- Be a good role model. Take good care of yourself. Demonstrate positive ways that you manage stress, anger, sadness, and other difficult emotions.

- Remember that they have to do the work. If you try to solve the problems for them, it is sending the message that you do not have faith in them.

- Ask for help. No one can be the complete and only source of strength for someone struggling with an eating disorder. When you ask for help from others, you are taking good care of yourself and your loved one, while also being a good role model.

- Demonstrate compassion. Often, people just need someone to listen without judgment or criticism.

- Accept that this will be an ongoing journey for your loved one. The eating disorder did not develop overnight, and the healing process will not happen overnight.

- Ask what you can do to help. Throughout recovery, people will learn to ask for and seek out help.

- Learn to use "I" messages with your loved one. For example, "I feel _____ when you _____; please _____. (e.g, "I feel scared when you purge; please stop.")

- Remember, recovery is a painful process. It will take tremendous courage and energy for your loved one to face the painful emotions and experiences that they have been trying to suppress. Be patient, kind, and supportive.

- Encourage your loved one to seek professional help.

# HOW TO ACHIEVE THE BEAUTIFUL YOU

# PART 3

# WHAT IS BEAUTIFUL ANYWAY?

Before you read the definition of beauty that I provide, take a minute to think about the answer for yourself. If you are so inclined, write it down here before we move on.

BEAUTIFUL MEANS: _____

_____

_____

_____

_____

_____

One way that humans learn is by watching and listening to others. In each and every culture, there are different attributes to define what is beautiful.

## BEAUTY DEFINITION

The *Merriam-Webster* definition of beauty is as follows:

*Main Entry:* beau•ty

*Pronunciation:* 'byü-tE

*Function: noun*

*Inflected Form(s): plural* **beauties**

*Etymology:* Middle English *beaute*, from Old French *biauté*, from *bel*, *beau*, beautiful, from Latin *bellus*, pretty; akin to Latin *bonus* good — more at *bounty*

**1:** the quality or aggregate of qualities in a person or thing that gives pleasure to the senses or pleasurably exalts the mind or spirit: *loveliness*

**2:** a *beautiful* person or thing; *especially*: a *beautiful* woman

**3:** a particularly graceful, ornamental, or excellent quality

**4:** a brilliant, extreme, or egregious example or instance <that mistake was a *beauty*>

# A MATTER OF CONTROL?

In the process of doing research for this book, I learned that many scientific studies and researchers have suggested that people struggling with eating disorders are trying to establish a sense of control in their out-of-control world. For example, Marianne cannot control that her father left the house one day to go and get cigarettes and never came back. She also cannot control that her mother began drinking heavily once her father left. Marianne did report to me that she could control what she put in and out of her body. Is it that our society has placed an emphasis on skinnier being "more in control"?

According to Robert Biswas-Diener *(Be Beautiful and Carry a Big Stick)* at www.clamormagazine.org,

> Other societies can demonstrate this point. The Masai people of South Africa to this date have no history of eating disorders. Their definition of beauty is somewhat different than that of the United States. A beautiful person is defined as having white teeth, short hair, and elongated ear lobes. The Masai seem to have some control over the characteristics that define beauty in their life. If they wish to have whiter teeth, they can brush them. If they want to have short hair, it is just a matter of grooming. If they wish to have elongated ear lobes, it is just a stretching process. I might also wonder what happens to those who wish to take beauty to the "extreme" in their culture. They would over brush their teeth, have the most elongated ear lobes, and the shortest hair possible. The interesting part is that none of these choices would be harmful to the individual.
>
> In America, beauty is often defined by who is young, the most fit, the best complexion and who has the largest breasts. Americans have begun to use technology to try and get the definition of most beautiful through using plastic surgery. The problem for those seeking to look younger with plastic surgery is that even though they have a procedure that makes them look younger, it does not actually make them any younger. Or, if someone has liposuction to remove fat to look more fit and healthy, the procedure does not actually make the person more fit and healthy. Just because Patty has liposuction one day certainly does not mean she can compete in a triathlon the next month. Her appearance may seem healthier, but she is not fit or healthier. The challenge [is] how do we embrace who we are—all the good and not so good points and live our life to the fullest. We might have been taught to look young, but there is only one alternative to growing old and most of us do not like to face that challenge either.

# WHAT THE MEDIA HAS TAUGHT US

Have you even challenged yourself to think about the messages that we learn as we are growing up? Let's see if you have ever heard these messages:

- You can never be too rich or too thin.

- Thin is in.

- Fat people are lazy.

- Being beautiful will make you happier, more successful, make people like you more, and get that dream boyfriend/girlfriend that you are waiting for.

- Dieting demonstrates motivation.

So what does it really mean to be beautiful? A lot of people formulate their definition of beauty by viewing, reading, and listening to American media. Think of Michael Jackson. I know he does not admit to any plastic surgery, but let's compare him in the 1970s to present-day. He looks quite different. Let's now pretend that American culture has begun to promote fashion/beauty models that resemble Michael Jackson. He is the now the standard of American beauty. Are you willing to change yourself the way he has in order to fit in? To be liked?

What media messages do you currently follow? _____

_____

_____

_____

_____

_____

Challenge yourself to be comfortable in your own skin. Embrace the qualities that you have been given. Celebrate your differences. The day that you make the choice to accept yourself and define your own beauty will be the day that you *realize* your great beauty. Often, I will meet people who have been on such a journey of becoming the media's definition of what ideal beauty is that they have lost who they are. They have forgotten what their passions are. The more they become focused on outward beauty, the more they lose what truly makes them beautiful in the first place.

What are your inner passions? A good way to rediscover what your passions are is to take a moment out of your day to pretend you have all the money and time in the world. If you had all the money and time in the world, what would you spend your time doing? If you knew you only had five more years of health, what would you want to do, see, feel, or experience?

_____

_____

_____

_____

_____

_____

_____

_____

_____

_____

_____

_____

# JULIE'S STORY

I often think of Julie, the girl with the broken smile. Julie and I had determined together that there are many different types of smiles. All in all, she determined that she had around 12 smiles that she recognized. There was the camera smile. Someone grabs a camera and tells her to smile. This was a forced smile, and no one really paid attention that she just used the muscles on her face to form the smile; it was just because someone told her that she needed to do it. There was her true smile—whenever she would just burst out with a true, soulful, passionate laugh. People used to tell her that smile would actually brighten up a room. She had not heard that in a while. She often tried to walk around with a smile, but it seemed broken. There was no passion, happiness, or joy in the smile. She only wore it hoping to hide the pain. By this point, the pain was so overwhelming, her smile did nothing to cover it. Her smile was broken. You see, she had been living by other people's rules so long, she had lost herself. Her mother was a small and meek woman who was unsure of herself and had never learned to assert herself. Therefore, Julie had embraced the same characteristics.

Julie's world changed when she met up with her boyfriend (now husband) at the tender age of 16. She adored getting attention, and initially felt great when she was around him. He and his family, however, embraced different characteristics than her family. They embraced materialism and outward appearance as their personal means of feeling some control and self-worth in the world. Therefore, the more things they had, the thinner they were, and the better they looked characterized what was successful. So Julie began to obsess about her outer appearance and to insist on having material goods to demonstrate her value in the world. She now spent her time shopping, getting her nails done, getting her hair done, and hoping that she would be noticed. As Julie began to get more praise from others about her outward appearance, her mother-in-law and sister-in-law became increasingly jealous. They would begin to make comments that Julie was lazy and just not all that intelligent. These statements were completely untrue, but because Julie had begun to obsess about her outward appearance, she had lost the real Julie. She lost her balance, her confidence, her passions, and her friends.

Julie's girlfriends still were enjoying what Julie had enjoyed with them in the past—going out to movies, going swimming, and hanging out at the bookstore. Julie did not have time to sit and chat at the bookstore. She used to love grabbing a magazine and giggling with her friends. She no longer went swimming at the beach with them. She now was saying that she was unworthy of being in a bathing suit. And, going to the movies was out of the question, because her entire budget went toward managing her appearance. She bought all the fashion magazines, all the new beauty products, all the diet food, all the new fashions, and actually had a running tab going at the salon. She had traded her joys and passions to focus on her outward appearance. Her inner beauty was starving.

# JUST THE FACTS, MA'AM

How many people do you know now who are on a diet? Consider the following facts:

- Diet and diet related products are a 33-billion dollar per year industry.

- 35% of occasional dieters progress into pathological dieting.

- Two out of five women and one out of five men would trade three to five years of their life to achieve their weight goals.

- In 1970, the average age a girl began dieting was 14; by 1990, the average age dropped to 8.

- One half of 4th-grade girls are on a diet.

- 51% of 9- and 10-year-old girls stated they felt better about themselves when they were adhering to a diet.

- Frequent dieting is highly correlated with depression.

- While only 1 out of 10 high school girls are overweight, 9 out of 10 high school junior and senior girls diet.

- 79% of teenage girls who vomit and 73% of teenage girls who use diet pills are frequent readers of women's health and fitness magazines. This is in contrast to less than 43% of teenage girls who do not participate in these purging methods.

- One out of three women and one out of four men are on a diet at any given time.

- Women frequently compare their bodies to those they see around them, and researchers have found that exposure to idealized body images lowers women's satisfaction with their own attractiveness.

- One study found that people who were shown slides of thin models had lower self-evaluations than people who had seen average and oversized models.

- Girls reported in a body image survey that "very thin" models made them feel insecure about themselves.

- In a sample of Stanford undergraduate and graduate students, 68% felt worse about their own appearance after looking through women's magazines.

- 75% of "normal" weight women think they are overweight.

- 90% of women overestimate their body size.

- The number one wish for girls ages 11 to 17 is to be thinner.

- Girls as young as five have expressed fears of getting fat.

- 80% of 10-year-old girls have dieted.

- At any given time, 50% of American women are currently dieting.

- Some researchers suggest depicting thin models may lead girls into unhealthy weight-control habits because the ideal they seek to emulate is unattainable for many and unhealthy for most.

- One study found that 47% of girls were influenced by magazine pictures to want to lose weight, but only 29% were actually overweight.

- Research has found that stringent dieting to achieve an ideal figure can play a key role in triggering eating disorders.

- Researchers believe depicting thin models appears not to have long-term negative effects on most adolescent women, but they do agree it affects girls who already have body-image problems.

- Girls who were already dissatisfied with their bodies showed more dieting, anxiety, and bulimic symptoms after prolonged exposure to fashion and advertising images in a teen girl magazine.

- Studies show that a third of American women in their teens and 20s begin smoking cigarettes in order to help control appetite.

- The majority of teenagers with eating disorders are girls (90%).

- Experts believe the number of boys affected is increasing and that many cases may not be reported, since males are reluctant to acknowledge any illness primarily associated with females.

- Studies have found that boys, like girls, may turn to smoking to help them lose weight.

- Boys ages 9 to 14 who thought they were overweight were 65% more likely to think about or try smoking than their peers, and boys who worked out every day in order to lose weight were twice as likely to experiment with tobacco.

(Above facts collected from the following sources: Schneider, K. "Mission Impossible." People Magazine, June, 1996; Dittrich, L. "About-Face Facts on the MEDIA"; Maynard, C. "Body Image." Current Health 2, 1998; Kilbourne, J., "Slim Hopes," video, Media Education Foundation, 1995; Media Influence on Teens; "Facts on Body and Image"; Kilbourne, J., Schneider, K., Woznicki, K. "Pop Culture Hurts Body Image." OnHealth Website, 1999.

(http://www.onhealth.com/ch1/briefs/item,55572.asp). Last retrieved April 13, 2000; "Magazine Models Impact Girls' Desire to Lose Weight," press release; "Facts on Body and Image"; Goode, E. "Girls' Self Image Survives Effect of Glossy Ads." The New York Times, August 24, 1999; Morris, L. "The Cigarette Diet." Allure, March 2000; Shallek-Klein, J. "Striving for the Baywatch Boy Build." Silver Chips Newspaper, October 7, 1999; "Body Image Disorder Linked to Toy Action Figures' Growing Muscularity." McLean Hospital press release, 1999; Schneider, K., Wax, R. G. "Boys and Body Image." San Diego Parent Magazine, 1998; Marcus, A. "Body Image Tied to Smoking in Kids." Health Scout. Merck-Medco Managed Care, 1999.)

# QUICK REFERENCE

❖ "The average model weighs 23% less than the average woman. Maintaining a weight that is 15% below your expected body weight fits the criteria for anorexia, so most models, according to medical standards, fit into the category of being anorexic." ("Facts on Body and Image," compiled by Jean Holzgang. Just Think Foundation Website. [http://www.justthink.org/bipfact.html . Last retrieved April 14, 2000]).

❖ Twenty years ago the average model weighed 8% less than the average woman.

❖ Today, top models are 5' 9" to 6' and weigh 110 to 118 pounds, even though the average woman is 5' 4" and weighs 142 pounds. And consider the Pacific island of Fiji. Islanders first encountered television in 1995. Immediately, there was a sharp rise in eating disorders. Just over three years after the tube's introduction, 74% of girls reported feeling "too big" or "too fat." "Nobody was dieting in Fiji ten years ago," says Harvard Medical School anthropology professor Anne Becker. "The teenagers see TV as a model for how one gets by in the modern world. They believe the shows depict reality." (Plugged In. Copyright © 2000 Focus on the Family. All rights reserved. International copyright secured.)

❖ Clinical psychologist and *Reviving Ophelia* (1994, New York: Random House) author Mary Pipher reports, "Research shows that virtually all women are ashamed of their bodies. It used to be adult women [and] teenage girls who were ashamed, but now you see the shame down to very young girls—10, 11 years old. Society's standard of beauty is an image that is literally just short of starvation for most women" (pp. 183–185).

❖ 81% of 10-year-olds are afraid of being fat. 51% of 9- and 10-year-old girls feel better about themselves if they are on a diet (L. Mellin, S. McNutt, Y. Hu, G. B. Schreiber, P. Crawford, & E. Obarzanek, 1991, *Journal of Adolescent Health*, 27–37).

❖ The average woman is 5' 4" tall and weighs 140 pounds. The average American model is 5' 11" tall and weighs 117 pounds. Most fashion models are thinner than 98% of American women.

❖ 91% of women recently surveyed on a college campus had attempted to control their weight through dieting; 22% dieted "often" or "always" (C. L. Kurth, D. D. Krahn, K. Nairn, & A. Drewnowski, 1995, *Journal of Psychiatric Research,* 29[3], 211–225).

❖ 35% of "normal dieters" progress to pathological dieting (C. M. Shisslak, M. Crago, & L. S. Estes, 1995, *Journal of Eating Disorders, 18*[3], 209–219). Diet and diet related products are a 33-billion dollar per year industry (K. Schneider, June 3, 1996, "Mission Impossible." *People Weekly*.).

❖ Repeated exposure to the thin ideal via various media can lead to the internalization of this ideal. It also renders these images real and achievable. Until women are confronted with their own mirror images, they will continue to measure themselves against an inhuman ideal (E. A. Dittrich, 1997, Dissertation Abstracts International, California Institute of Integral Studies).

❖ Thinness has not only come to represent attractiveness, but also has come to symbolize success, self-control, and higher socioeconomic status.

❖ Marketdata Enterprises, Inc. estimated the size of the weight loss industry for 1994 at $32,680 billion (MarketData Enterprise Inc., Tampa, FL, 813-931-3900).

# CONSIDER THE MARKETING MACHINE

Take just one day to determine the number of diet/exercise commercials constantly appearing on your television screens, telling you that once you lose weight you will be happy. Pay attention while standing in the checkout line at the grocery store where you are surrounded by magazines claiming to have the newest and best diet. Each month another new diet appears claiming to be the diet to end all diets. Whatever happened to last month's diet that claimed the same thing?

Consider your answers to the following:

How many fitness commercials do you see every day? What is the definition of fitness on these commercials?

How many diet commercials do you see every day? What is the diet's definition of healthy?

How many reality shows do you see promoting weight loss? What is their definition of healthy?

How many actors/actresses can you find that look like you?

How many actors/actresses can you find that look like your family and/or friends?

How many commercials do you see for beauty products?

What messages are the media sending you about your beauty?

# WHAT DOES IT MEAN TO BE FAT?

Take a moment to jot down what comes to mind when you think of the following words:

FAT    _____

HIPS    _____

OVERWEIGHT    _____

THIGHS    _____

SKINNY    _____

Now take a moment to review what you wrote. I give this exercise to professionals all over the United States, in part to help them teach others body acceptance. I took a poll from 26 separate states and came up with similar answers across the nation. So please don't be surprised if many of your answers match the answers of the professionals in this study. I will share the most common answers.

For FAT: me (meaning that they are fat), lazy, unhealthy, and stupid

For HIPS: fat, childbearing, wide, large, and swinging

For OVERWEIGHT: aches and pains, sweaty, stupid, disgusting, heart attack, and afraid to be overweight

For THIGHS: thunder (number one answer, as in "thunder thighs") Other common answers included chubby, cellulite, thick, fat and large.

For SKINNY: "I wish I could be," or "I used to be," or "I never have been" (number one answers) and self-discipline

The most important part of this exercise is self-awareness. When you consider what definitions you give words, know that they often have altered meanings that you have picked up from the media, family, and/or friends. For example, the Oxford Dictionary's definition of fat is "a highly concentrated reserve of energy; insulation/body heat and/or a buffer to absorb shock in the areas of the body that experience frequent impact of pressure." I can tell you that if someone calls you fat, you probably attribute it to negative connotations far removed from the

Oxford definition. If someone calls you fat, you probably are thinking that they also are implying you are lazy, unhealthy, and stupid. What if you allowed yourself to follow the actual Oxford Dictionary definition? Then, if someone called you fat, you would think, "Hey, they can recognize my highly concentrated reserve of energy." Sounds really silly, right? How about for thighs? Have you ever considered that your thighs are one of the major muscle groups that help you walk upright?

Wouldn't it be nice to begin thinking of our body parts by their true definitions of function and not as fashion? We are allowed to change the negative definitions we have created for our bodies—what I call the "negative weight" of our minds. Try to write down definitions that you would like to think of. Then, begin believing the positive definitions. It certainly can be a first step to learning to love and appreciate your body and dropping the "negative weight." You are worth it.

My New Definitions . . .

FAT _____

HIPS _____

OVERWEIGHT _____

THIGHS _____

SKINNY _____

# YOUR STRESS THERMOMETER

As we go through our days, little things begin to increase our internal stress thermometer. For example, can you imagine a day where you wake up late, don't have time to eat, there is a lot of traffic so you're late for work, you get a flat tire, you try to change the flat tire, it begins to rain, someone drives by and splashes water on you, you get to work and your coworker says that your boss wants to see you immediately? Your boss is not understanding about your morning, and you get written up. When you get home, you see that someone left a plate in the sink and you freak out. Your stress was not about the plate; it was about everything else that happened to you that day. Often it is good to get a read on your own personal stress thermometer. Where do you think you fall today? What are the experiences in your life that raise your stress thermometer? Do you eat more whenever you are stressed? What are the ways you lower your stress thermometer?

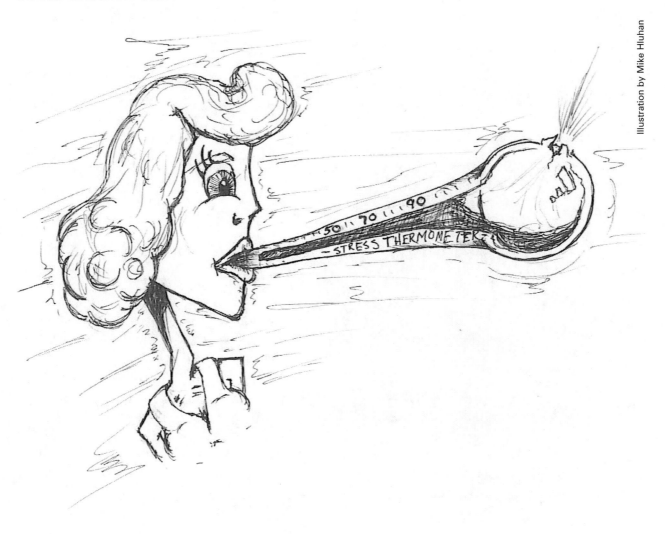

Illustration by Mike Hluhan

75

# MOTIVATION

So what is your definition of motivation? My opinion is that motivation is a feeling. Sometimes you feel emotions intensely; sometimes you are not feeling them at all. For example, when you watch a scary movie, you can be quite scared. When you walk out of the movie, you often do not feel scared at all anymore. On January 1, you feel intense motivation to achieve your goals. By January 3, you often do not feel motivation to achieve those goals at all.

Another definition of motivation can be your inspiration to keep moving forward. With this definition, you can begin to define what inspires you to drop the negative weight and add in the love you deserve.

Truth be told, research shows that the more motivation you have to complete a task, the higher the chances are that you will achieve your goal. Write down your motivations to love your body:

_____

_____

_____

_____

_____

_____

_____

_____

_____

_____

_____

_____

# IMAGINE

In order to help you "imagine" a healthier life without the negative weight, here are some examples and a few questions to ponder.

❖ Imagine having fulfilling relationships. (People often describe the walls they put up in relationships to keep themselves safe. The walls will get higher with the more negative weight you add.)

What would it be like to feel spontaneous again?

What would it be like to not worry about your appearance and focus instead on enjoying the people around you?

Illustration by Mike Hluhan

79

❖ Imagine putting yourself first. (Often people will share with me that when it comes to the list of things they need to do today, they are the last person on the list.)

What would it be like to put yourself first?

Illustration by Mike Hluhan

❖ Imagine listening to your mind, body, and spirit. (Learning to listen to what your body, mind, and spirit need are three separate journeys, each of equal value.)

Are you able to determine when your body is physically hungry?

Are you able to determine when your body is physically full?

Are you able to determine when your body is tired?

Are you able to determine when your body is energized?

Are you able to determine when your mind is overwhelmed?

Are you able to determine when your mind is calm?

Are you able to determine when your mind is relaxed?

Are you able to determine when your mind is happy?

Are you able to determine where you are on your spiritual journey?

Do you have spiritual goals?

❖ Imagine laughing more. (Laughter truly is the best medicine.)

When is the last time you laughed?

What makes you laugh?

Can you try and get one good belly laugh a day?

❖ Imagine having extra time to play instead of worrying about your weight.

How much time do you spend worrying every day about your weight?

How much time do you spend worrying every day about your appearance?

What would you rather be spending your time doing?

❖ Imagine being clear of medical problems.

❖ Imagine more activities you enjoy.

What are the activities that you always have wanted to try?

❖ Imagine having more money.

If looks and appearance did not matter, what would you spend your money on?

❖ Imagine more self-confidence.

What would life be like without that mean voice in your head?

# MY TOOLBOX

1. The Tool of Honesty

   Honesty truly is a tool. Since you began to veer off your path of healthy food and body image, you have begun to be dishonest with yourself. The farther away from the path of health, the more lies that you have created. Remember:

   - The prettiest lie will make you weaker, and the ugliest truth will make you stronger.

   - Telling a lie puts the problem in your future, telling the truth puts the problem in your past.

2. The Tool of Accepting Help

   Let's be honest. (I have that tool already, so I can.) Most people have to learn to accept help from others. It will be important that you take inventory of your life to determine who can help and what each person is good at. I agree that you need to find the right person for the job. It can be very frustrating to go to a friend in hopes that they will listen to your struggle, and all they suggest is going to see a movie and not talking about it. One generalization is that there are three types of helpers in the world—good listeners, doers (or pitchers), and avoiders (or activity directors). Depending on what we are struggling with at any given time, we may need any one of the three types of helpers:

   - Good Listeners—These are people able to sit and listen and actually hear what you have to say. They are not distracted and pay attention to everything you say. They care about the problem you are currently facing. They are the non-judgmental friends who will not give you advice unless you ask for it.

   - Pitchers—These are people who will pitch in and help with anything that you need. If you are sick, they will bring you chicken soup. If you break a leg, they will come over and clean your house. They will do things to show you that they care.

   - Activity Directors—These are people who will take you out to have some fun. They do not want to talk about the problems; they want you to take a break from it and enjoy life.

Make a list of your friends and family, determining which type of helper each is:

| PERSON | HELPER TYPE |
|---|---|
| _____ | _____ |
| _____ | _____ |
| _____ | _____ |
| _____ | _____ |
| _____ | _____ |
| _____ | _____ |
| _____ | _____ |
| _____ | _____ |
| _____ | _____ |
| _____ | _____ |

### 3. The Tool of Setting Limits and Boundaries

Limits and boundaries are difficult to define and even more difficult to adhere to. Life is very chaotic without limits and boundaries. For example, imagine what driving would be like without any limits. Someone would drive 10 miles per hour and someone would drive 100 miles per hour. There would be no stop signs or signals. A lot more people would get hurt. Without setting limits and boundaries within your life, you can get hurt as well. Set limits for your:

| | |
|---|---|
| Relationships | Exercise |
| Work | Appearance |
| Play | The little voice in your head |
| Nutrition | Anything and everything in your life that is out of balance |

### 4. The Tool of Being Gentle with Yourself

If you are not going to learn how to be nice to yourself, how can you expect anyone else to? Make a goal to become your own best friend. What are the steps to take to become your own best friend?

# WHAT CONTROLS MY EATING HABITS?

When it comes down to it, the majority of Americans are no longer connected to listening to their bodies. Our bodies let us know when we are hungry. Our bodies also signal us to stop eating when we feel full. Instead of following these internal signals, we opt instead to listen to numerous other factors that affect our choices of what, when, and where we eat. For example, have you ever overeaten because it was a holiday? Realistically, it does not really make any sense that a day on a calendar can control our eating habits, does it? Do you still define your current eating habits from the culture that you grew up in?

My culture affects my appetite by: _____

_____

_____

My family affects my appetite by: _____

_____

_____

Holidays and/or celebrations affect my appetite by: _____

_____

_____

I find myself "emotionaly eating" when I feel: _____

_____

_____

How hungry I am affects my appetite by: _____

_____

_____


Other people affect my choices of food by: _____

_____

_____


The choices of food available affect my appetite by: _____

_____

_____


Dieting has affected my behavior by: _____

_____

_____

# 10 OUTSTANDING TIPS FOR EVERYBODY

### 1. Stop Talking About Your Weight (especially in front of young girls)

Young girls listen to the way women talk about themselves and each other and learn the language of womanhood. Young women can only learn to love or even accept their bodies if they see women who love and accept their own. Every discussion we have about weight, or fat, or being too this or that, leaves an impression on the people around us. We are encouraging an unattainable quest for perfection.

### 2. Make a List of Women You Admire

How often is the woman's appearance a reason that you admire her? What do you think are the most important attributes a woman can have? What would you like a young woman to most admire in you? In herself? Does our culture seem to admire the same things in women that you do?

### 3. Question the Motives of the Fashion Industry

Always remember that the main objective of the fashion, cosmetic, diet, fitness, and plastic surgery industries is to make money, not to make you the best person you can possibly be. The ultra thin ideal is working for them. But is it working for you? If every season your parent or partner told you to change who you are or how you dress, wouldn't you question their motives?

### 4. Stop Weighing Yourself

Remember that the emphasis to be thin and beautiful is ever-present in our society. Cut yourself some slack. Imagine spending a day, or a week, without the scale measuring your self-esteem. Does the scale tell you that you aren't disciplined enough? That you aren't working hard enough? Get rid of it. The emphasis on thin is new and arbitrary. And it can be reversed.

### 5. Concentrate on Things You Do Well

Do you look in the mirror one day and think you look great and the next day think you look awful? Your body isn't changing; your perception of it is. It is true that if you're feeling good about other things in your life, you'll be less critical of how you look. Do things you do well. And if you've had a bad day, stay away from the mirror. When a woman is happy and confident, she may not have a "perfect" body, but she doesn't care.

### 6. Get Physical for Fun

Your body needs EXERCISE and REAL FOODS. Take walks, dance in your living room, garden, golf . . . try to get moving for your heart, not to decrease the size of your bottom. You may lose weight and you may not, but your body will be stronger, your stress will be lower, and you'll feel better.

### 7. Value Your Dollars

With more women working outside the home today than ever before, our dollars are much in demand. You are being courted! How much of your money goes into the fashion and cosmetics industries? What do you spend on eating regimens? What are you getting back? Look at your budget and be sure the money you spend reflects the person you are, not the person society wants you to be. If looks didn't matter at all, what would you spend your money on?

### 8. Voice Your Opinion

Both large and small businesses are interested in your input. Your letters and phone calls really make a difference. The following organizations can help you find the addresses of companies. Contact Media Action Alliance in Circle Pines, MN (612-434-4343) or Media Watch in Santa Cruz, CA (408-423-6355). Subscribe to Media Watch's terrific quarterly "Action Agenda."

### 9. Be a Role Model

Every culture and every generation has its own rules and expectations for women. It is never easy to go against the grain, but there always have been women who took risks to grow and learn and succeed. And there always will be. Many inspirational women have broken molds, set new standards, and blazed trails. Wouldn't you like to break a mold or two?

### 10. Break the Barriers

Author Sara Tisdale wrote, "We must all choose between battles: One battle is against the cultural ideal, and the other is against ourselves." Must we always define ourselves by what popular culture dictates? Develop your own style. Have fun—Wear lipstick. Or don't. You're the boss of you. By speaking out and accepting yourself (dimples and all), you help break the barriers.

(Copyright © 1996–2004 About-Face, about-face.org. All rights reserved.)

# HOW I FEEL ABOUT MY BODY

Color in the figure below indicating how you feel about your body parts.

Use RED for the body parts that you do not like.

Use GREEN for the body parts you do like.

Use YELLOW for the body parts that are neutral.

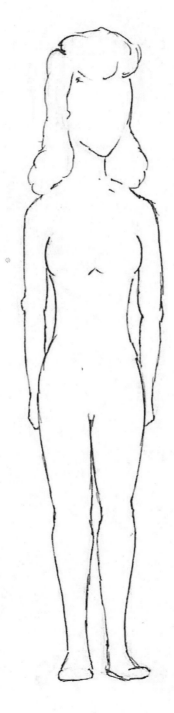

Illustration by Mike Hluhan

89

Now take a look at the picture. Are there more things that you dislike about your body than you like?

Why do you dislike these parts of your body?

How does holding on to disliking each body part help you?

How would your life change if the next supermodel looked exactly like you? What if the body parts that you have colored in red suddenly are considered beautiful by the media? Would you still want to change them?

Take a look at the body parts that you like. Why do you like them?

Do you allow yourself any time in the day to focus on the body parts that you already like? Would you like to spend more time focusing on them?

# WHAT ARE THE GREAT THINGS ABOUT ME?

Color in the figure below with all the beautiful things about yourself.

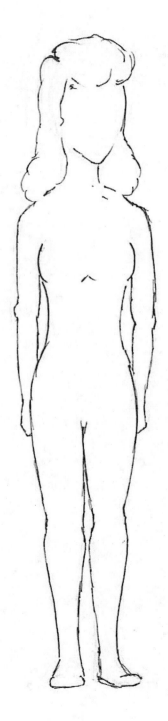

Illustration by Mike Hluhan

What do you want to fill up more with?

What qualities do you respect in others? Can you add any of these qualities to yourself?

What is more important—how beautiful someone is on the inside or on the outside?

Draw a picture of how you look on the inside:

# LISTENING

Most people struggle with just wishing someone would listen to them. A very challenging assignment is to listen to the most important person in your life—YOU. This assignment helps guide and categorize your thinking. This work is adapted from Aaron Beck's Cognitive Behavioral Theory.

This assignment involves three steps.

**STEP ONE**: Get a journal and make a commitment that you will write in it every day. I know, I know—not everyone feels like journaling is fit for them. Do what works for you. I once knew a woman who would write down all of her thoughts on napkins, put them in her purse, and bring them with her to each session. The important part is making the commitment to you. So . . . you make the commitment, and now what? Take some time each day and listen to how you talk with yourself. This is sometimes a very powerful emotional experience and can be quite overwhelming. Try to just monitor what you say to yourself without judgment.

**STEP TWO**: Take time to read and understand the thought patterns shown below. Take a long, hard look at your current journal and determine if you feel that any of your thoughts fit into these patterns.

## THOUGHT PATTERNS

1. All or Nothing Thinking

   **Definition**: Thinking in extremes with no middle ground. (I am good or bad, a success or complete failure, skinny or fat, etc.)

   **True Life Example**: One client received the first B of her entire academic career as a senior in high school. When I saw her in session after she received the B, she tried to convince me that she was stupid. Her proof was that she now had a B and there was no such thing as a middle ground with her thoughts. Another client determined her feelings about herself by what number the scale read every morning. If the number read one pound over where she felt she needed to be, she considered herself fat. If she was under the number she felt she needed to be at, she would say she was "okay." There was no in between or happy middle ground.

## 2. Overgeneralization

**Definition**: To take an isolated event and make it a broad general rule.

**True Life Example**: I have a friend who feels like she thinks better if she pulls on her right ear. She explained that she was struggling on a test in middle school and pulled on her right ear. At that very moment, she recalled the answer she needed and ended up doing very well on her exam. Anytime I am struggling to remember something, she often tells me to just pull on my right ear and I will remember. When her technique does not help me to recall, she just tells me I am not doing it right. Another example would be a female client, Judy, explaining that in sixth grade Johnny called her fat. Johnny never called her fat again, but from that point forward Judy overgeneralized that everyone else must think she is fat and decided that for people to like her she would need to stop eating. Johnny still has no idea of the torment that Judy endured because of that one comment. Another example would be a father telling her daughter that she was ugly, and she now believes every male thinks she is ugly.

## 3. Mislabeling

**Definition**: Taking one small fault and believing that everything about you is at fault.

**True Life Example**: I could perceive the fact that I have poor vision as a fault. I can then say that since I do not have perfect vision, I am not perfect. If I am not perfect then I do not deserve to be in a happy relationship, hold a fulfilling job, have loyal friends, or be happy. You probably would tell me that I am ridiculous, but with mental filtering, one small perceived deficiency can cause us extreme emotional pain in other areas of life. Another example of this distortion would be a client who called herself the "recovered beauty queen." Even though she had been crowned the winner of over 30 beauty pageants, she would continue to believe, "I have fat thighs, so I am not beautiful." She obviously had been chosen as "most beautiful" according to beauty pageant standards, but she refused to see any other information presented to her.

## 4. Mental Filtering

**Definition**: This is focusing on the negative.

**True Life Example**: A good example that clearly demonstrates mental filtering was a lovely 13-year-old young lady named Jessica who showed up late for one of her appointments. When Jessica arrived, she apologized profusely and wiped the sweat from her brow. The sweat had accumulated from the stop she made at the library before coming to the office and then lugging the books with her all the way to the office. When I inquired about the books, she said with some authority, "Well, it was report card day." Knowing Jessica has always been a straight-A student, I furrowed my brow and asked how she did on her report card. Jessica stated she got straight As again. I then asked the obvious question of why she needed to stop at the library if she did such an outstanding job on her report card. Jessica stated that her very best friend, Tammy, had made a comment that upset her. Tammy took one look at Jessica's report card and said, "I hate you. I really do. You got straight As again. You have lettered in two sports and you can play the piano. The only thing that I can do half as good as you is with my handwriting. I think I am pretty good at that." Jessica did not hear all the compliments Tammy gave her; she only heard that Tammy felt that she was better at handwriting then Jessica was. So, on the way to the office, Jessica stopped by the library, got every book she could find on handwriting, and planned to spend the rest of the evenings ahead working on her handwriting.

## 5. Disqualifying the Positive

**Definition**: People who cannot accept any positive statements.

**True Life Example**: Have you ever given a compliment? Have you ever given a compliment that you did not really mean? Most of us will not go out of our way just to lie to another person. My 42-year-old client, Penny, often shared the compliments that other people would give her. She never would believe them. She became an expert at explaining away other people's observations of her. Penny often would say, "He only says those nice things because he wants me to like him" or "She only said that because she wants something from me." Remember, each and every one of us has wonderful things about us. Others are allowed to share our gifts with us. When someone goes out of the way to point out what is great in you and then you do not accept the compliment, you are rejecting his/her love and affection by throwing it back in his/her face.

## 6. Emotional Reasoning

**Definition**: Emotional reasoning is turning your personal feelings into facts.

**True Life Example**: Boy, do I really wish that this worked. For example, "I feel fat, so therefore I am fat" or "I feel like they don't like me, so therefore they don't like me." If this reasoning worked, then so would, "I feel like I am going to hit the lottery today, so therefore I will." We all agree that emotional reasoning does not work, but people continue to insist that their feelings immediately turn into fact.

7.  Should, Could, Would Statements

**Definition**: People who hold themselves to unrealistic expectations.

**True Life Example**: I need to let you know that these are dirty words. You can add them to all the other four letter words that we have been taught not to say in polite company. My opinion about these words is that they often lead to neurotic guilt. Let me give you an example of healthy guilt. We are both out at a restaurant in downtown Fort Myers. You are enjoying scrumptious cuisine and delightful company when I accidentally trip on my way to the bathroom and spill your drink all down the front of your brand new white shirt. Bear with me, guilt is part of a healthy, moral individual. Healthy guilt allows me to feel badly about hurting something or someone other than myself. With my healthy guilt, I apologize to you, get you something to wear, and offer to pay for your dry cleaning. You forgive me, finish your meal, and never think of me again. Fast forward to three months later and I am still thinking that I should have paid for your meal, or I wish I would stop being so clumsy, or I could have worn different shoes and I never would have tripped. Should, could, or would statements are often unrealistic expectations, setting people up for ongoing disappointment and failure. Other common examples include: "I should have willpower," "I should be able to stop this," or "I should have known better."

8.  Personalization

**Definition**: This thought pattern finds an individual incorrectly taking the responsibility for other people's poor behavior.

**True Life Example**: A common example of this pattern of thinking is found in survivors of abuse. Victims of abuse often inappropriately accept the responsibility for the abuse. A common misinformed statement is, "I must have been responsible for the abuse since I did not resist and it went on for so long." This clearly is not true, because a victim of abuse often does not have the capacity or knowledge to resist the abuse.

**STEP THREE**: Determine if your thoughts match any of these common distorted thought patterns.

# THE POWER OF WORDS

A great example of the power of words was a woman named Tammy who shared with me part of her life story. In sixth grade, a fellow student looked at Tammy and said, "You are fat." From sixth grade through her late 30s, Tammy obsessed about her weight every day and refused to allow herself to go over 100 pounds. The young boy only called her "fat" once, but it helped to lead to an unhealthy obsession with her weight. Her ongoing battle with her appearance has led her to an ongoing struggle with an eating disorder that has put her into the hospital four times and a current battle with severe osteoporosis. I am sure that young sixth grade boy has no idea of the extent of damage his three words caused and just how powerful he has been in Tammy's life. What words have hurt you the most?

_____

_____

_____

_____

_____

_____

_____

# PERCEPTIONS

The power to love our bodies lies in our own perceptions. I often explain perception by asking people to look at a set of car keys. The perception of those keys to a 16-year-old kid is freedom, excitement, and happiness. That same set of car keys has the perception of anxiety and car insurance rates going up to the parents of that 16-year-old. Those keys can represent a weapon to a drunk driver, or grief to the friends of someone killed by a drunk driver. They are just keys, but they are perceived differently by each person. The same concept applies to our bodies. How many times have you had one day when you felt great about yourself and the very next day you walk by the mirror and cannot believe the fat blob standing in front of you? In reality, none of us changes that drastically overnight; our perceptions of self, however, can change by the second.

Consider George Bernard Shaw's story of a Native American elder describing his own inner struggles. The elder stated, "Inside of me there are two dogs. One of the dogs is mean and evil. The other dog is good. The mean dog fights the good dog all the time." When asked which dog wins, he reflected for a moment and replied, "The one I feed the most." Often times when we say that we "hate" our bodies, "I am too fat," "my butt is too big," "my belly is disgusting," "I look too fat in these pants," and so on, we are letting that mean dog win. I know the problem for me was that the more I fed the mean dog, the bigger and more vicious the dog became. The good dog was so defeated, worn out, and beat up that it no longer tried to fight at all and accepted defeat.

So, who are you letting win your internal struggle? Who do you want to win? You have the power to decide how the battle turns out. I cannot promise it will be easy, but no battle worth winning ever really is. And, I might challenge, this is the ultimate battle—you. So imagine yourself today as a newly elected leader of this battle and take time to take stock of which dog is winning. Take some time and make two columns on a piece of paper. One column will be for the good thoughts and one column will be for the bad thoughts. Throughout one day write down all the mean and nasty things you say to yourself. Take another day to write down the nice things that you say to yourself. Most people are quite shocked by how truly cruel they are to themselves. How is being cruel helping you? The answer to that question is that it doesn't help. Believe me, I have heard how saying cruel things to yourself is inspiring, keeps people determined, makes sure that things don't get worse or that people won't get fatter. That is honestly ridiculous. Being cruel keeps you hating yourself and your body.

Okay, so you just realized that you have been over-feeding the mean dog? Your marching orders in this battle now are to fill up the positive side of your list. Try some of these exercises:

1. *Accept a compliment.* Can you think of the last positive compliment that you have received? If you can't think of one, please allow yourself to pay attention to the next one that comes. Write it down and remember that most people will not go out of their way to make up a lie about someone just to give a compliment. Think about the last time that you gave a compliment that you really did not mean; it's probably tough to think of one. People only give compliments when they really mean them. So, next time you get a compliment, smile and thank the person for noticing you for part of your greatness. If you have trouble believing the statement, give yourself the time and permission to really think about another person's view of you.

2. *Give yourself a sweet nickname.* Try sweetheart, wonderful, cutie pie—anything that you wish someone would call you. It will feel weird using your personal nickname for a while, but you will get used to it, and you deserve it.

3. *Review each night what you did well that day.* Try focusing on small things. They make a big difference in life. You may choose to keep track and add to your list every day.

4. *Smile.* Smiling is a universal beauty that everyone agrees upon. Remember that thinking good things about yourself does not make you conceited. Conceited is having an exaggerated opinion of your abilities and feeling more important than others. That is a long way off from feeling good about you. Each and every one of us has fantastic, wonderful characteristics. It is just what you choose to focus on and what perception you choose to believe. It is when we embrace and focus on what is wonderful in each of us that we can pass on joy and wonder to ourselves and others.

# DESIDERATA

Go placidly amid the noise and the haste,
and remember what peace there may be in silence.
As far as possible without surrender,
be on good terms with all persons.
Speak your truth quietly and clearly;
and listen to others; even the dull and ignorant;
they too have their story.
Avoid loud and aggressive persons,
they are vexation to the spirit.
If you compare yourself with others,
you may become vain and bitter; for always
there will be greater and lesser persons than yourself.
Enjoy your achievements as well as your plans.
Keep interested in your own career, however humble;
it is a real possession in the changing fortunes of time.
Exercise caution in your business affairs;
for the world is full of trickery.
But let this not blind you to what virtue there is;
many persons strive for high ideals;
and everywhere life is full of heroism.
Be yourself. Especially, do not feign affection.
Neither be cynical about love,
for in the face of all aridity and disenchantment,
it is perennial as the grass.
Take kindly to the counsel of years,
gracefully surrendering the things of youth.
Nurture strength of spirit to shield you in sudden misfortune.
But do not distress yourself with imaginings;
many fears are born of fatigue and loneliness.
Beyond a wholesome discipline, be gentle with yourself.
You are a child of the universe,
no less than the trees and the stars;
you have a right to be here.

And whether or not it is clear to you,
no doubt the universe is unfolding as it should.
Therefore be at peace with God,
whatever you conceive God to be.
And whatever your labors and aspirations,
in the noisy confusion of life,
keep peace with your soul.
With all its sham, drudgery and broken dreams,
it is still a beautiful world.
Be careful. Strive to be happy.

*(Found in Old Saint Paul's Church, Baltimore, dated 1692, public domain)*

# LET GO . . .

To let go does not mean to stop caring. It means I can't do it for someone else.

To let go is not to cut myself off. It's the realization I can't control another.

To let go is to allow someone to learn from natural consequences.

To let go is to recognize when the outcome is not in my hands.

To let go is not to care for, but to care about.

To let go is not to fix, but to be supportive.

To let go is not to judge, but to allow another to be a human being.

To let go is not to expect miracles, but to take each day as it comes, and cherish myself in it.

To let go is not to criticize or regulate anybody, but to try to become what I dream I can be.

To let go is not to regret the past, but to grow and live for the future.

To let go is to fear less and love more.

# A QUOTE A DAY

Allow yourself to pick a quote that speaks to you. Remind yourself of the quote several times a day. Allowing new thoughts literally will open new pathways in your mind—one more step to dropping the negative weight.

*Happiness is when what you think, what you say,*
*and what you do are in harmony.*

—Mahatma Gandhi

*All of us are stars and deserve the right to twinkle.*

—Marilyn Monroe

*I want to know what sustains you from the inside—*
*when all else falls away.*
*I want to know if you can be alone with yourself,*
*and if you truly like the company you keep in the empty moments.*

—Oriah Mountain Dreamer

*And the day came when the risk it took to remain tight inside the bud*
*was more painful than the risk it took to blossom.*

—Anais Nin

*Nothing good ever comes from blaming others.*
*You can only change yourself.*

—A. B. Witt

*Nothing can bring you peace but yourself.*

—Ralph Waldo Emerson

*Always be a first-rate version of yourself,*
*instead of a second-rate version of somebody else.*

—Judy Garland

*Do what you can, with what you have, where you are.*

—Theodore Roosevelt

*A "No" uttered from the deepest conviction
is better and greater than a "Yes" merely uttered to please,
or what is worse, to avoid trouble.*

—Mahatma Gandhi

*Growing is a lifetime job,
and we grow most when we're down in the valleys,
where the fertilizer is.*

—Barbara Johnson

*And the trouble is, if you don't risk anything, you risk even more.*

—Erica Jong

# MAGAZINE CHALLENGE

Take your favorite magazine and cut out all the pictures that look like:

You

Your family

Your friends

Anyone you know

Did you have difficulty finding pictures that look like you or people in your life?

Don't be discouraged if you have trouble finding pictures. You are comparing yourself to pictures of people that make up 1% of the population and even then, the pictures are touched up.

# 10 DETAILS ABOUT YOUR FIRST STEPS TOWARD RECOVERY

1. An important objective is to determine what emotions you are trying to cope with and determine new coping skills.

2. Know that it takes tremendous courage, honesty, and energy to take these steps.

3. Your first steps are likely to be tentative and shaky. Even if you are scared, the challenge is to take the steps no matter what.

4. Determine your triggers. Make an inventory of the people, things, and situations that you believe contribute to your eating disorder; you will have a lot of important information to share with your treatment team.

5. Isolating your negative triggers will help you understand the logic of your eating disorder and change its patterns.

6. Relearning to eat and think about food in a non-eating-disordered way takes time, patience, and a strategy that makes sense and that you are willing to use.

7. Managing your fears of food, fat, and rejection will be challenging.

8. Remember every day that you are going to feel better than you ever have.

9. Relaxation and visualization techniques help you take the first steps toward recovery with more confidence and less tension.

10. A blueprint for the life you imagine living without the eating disorder (or with it in check) will connect you to a positive goal. Revise it every few weeks as you gain confidence in the process of change.

(Adapted from N. Kolodny, 2004, *The Beginner's Guide to Eating Disorder Recovery*, Carlsbad, CA: Gurze Books, pp. 97-118.)

# TRIGGERS

Our brain is an amazing organ. It stores, classifies, and organizes information every single second. Sometimes these memories make us feel good and safe. Other times, memories can hurt us. Our challenge is to determine what affects us the most. We are all unique and can learn to recognize and utilize our triggers for our own benefit.

## COMMON TRIGGERS FOR TURNING TO FOOD

- Low Self-Esteem, Inadequacy, Anxiety—Food can actually affect the chemicals in the brain to reduce feelings of anxiety and depression. The chemical reaction, however, is time-limited. Often that means that a person will get anxious, eat lots of chocolate, and feel better. Once that chocolate is metabolized, the anxiety returns and the person seeks chocolate again. On the other hand, people with high anxiety often will starve themselves of food because it will reduce the chemicals making them feel anxious. This works until the body recognizes the decrease in consumption of the chemical and will produce more of it again. Thus, the person will feel anxious again.

- Defining Self in Terms of Appearance—This is the "I am too fat for . . ." syndrome.

- Helplessness and Need for Control

- Difficulty in Managing Emotions—People often report being able to ignore a problem that is going on or "zoning out" from managing difficult emotions.

- Social Anxiety and Lack of Social Skills

- Fear of Growing Up

- Dysfunctional Home Life

- Negative Self-Talk—Saying mean things to yourself often will trigger issues with food.

Do any of these apply to you? Discuss other triggers that make you eat:

_____

_____

_____

_____

# YOU ARE MORE THAN JUST A SHAPE

You are more than just a shape.

You are hopes

You are dreams

You are a daughter/son

You are a mother/father

You are important

You are helpful

You are _____

# EMOTIONAL DIET

## PART 1

I tend to eat too much food when I'm feeling . . .

- ❑ Depressed
- ❑ Disappointed
- ❑ Unpopular
- ❑ Moody
- ❑ Frustrated
- ❑ Anxious
- ❑ Angry
- ❑ Overwhelmed
- ❑ Tired
- ❑ Impatient
- ❑ Afraid
- ❑ Helpless
- ❑ Nervous
- ❑ Annoyed
- ❑ Sick
- ❑ Embarrassed
- ❑ Jealous
- ❑ Upset
- ❑ Lonely
- ❑ Mad
- ❑ Confused
- ❑ Humiliated
- ❑ Guilty
- ❑ Confused

❑ Bored

❑ Ashamed

❑ Needy

❑ Unloved

❑ Worthless

❑ Abandoned

❑ Empty

❑ Other: _____

# PART 2

Eating gives me some temporary relief by making me feel . . .

❑ Rewarded

❑ In Control

❑ Loved

❑ Alive

❑ Wanted

❑ Peaceful

❑ Numb

❑ Confident

❑ Safe

❑ Secure

❑ Satisfied

❑ Content

❑ Relaxed

❑ Comfortable

❑ Calm

❑ Powerful

❑ Independent

❑ Capable

- ❑ Complete
- ❑ Comfortable
- ❑ Nurtured
- ❑ At Ease
- ❑ Happy
- ❑ Entertained

# PART 3

But, later I feel . . .

- ❑ Like a failure
- ❑ Like I'm sabotaging myself
- ❑ Weak
- ❑ Undeserving
- ❑ Hopeless
- ❑ Totally incapable of losing weight
- ❑ Crushed
- ❑ Worthless
- ❑ Depressed
- ❑ Disappointed
- ❑ Unpopular
- ❑ Moody
- ❑ Frustrated
- ❑ Anxious
- ❑ Angry
- ❑ Overwhelmed
- ❑ Tired
- ❑ Impatient
- ❑ Afraid
- ❑ Helpless

- ❏ Nervous
- ❏ Annoyed
- ❏ Sick
- ❏ Embarrassed
- ❏ Jealous
- ❏ Upset
- ❏ Lonely
- ❏ Mad
- ❏ Confused
- ❏ Humiliated
- ❏ Guilty
- ❏ Bored
- ❏ Ashamed
- ❏ Needy
- ❏ Unloved
- ❏ Abandoned
- ❏ Empty
- ❏ Drained
- ❏ Torn apart
- ❏ Insecure of my self-worth
- ❏ Ugly
- ❏ Other: _____

"When I'm feeling _____ (Part 1),

eating gives me some temporary relief by making me feel

_____ (Part 2),

but later I feel _____ (Part 3)."

**Example:**

"When I'm feeling anxious, eating gives me some temporary relief by making me feel at ease, but later I feel like a failure."

You are in control of changing the way you think. Please fill in the blanks according to what you want to think and feel:

I will now learn to deal with my _____ feeling.

I will now find other ways to feel _____.

I will no longer have to feel _____ after eating.

**Example:**

I will now learn to deal with my anxious feeling.

I will now find other ways to feel temporary relief.

I will no longer have to feel failure after eating.

# AFFIRMATIONS

People often learn to "kick out" the negative thoughts and do not learn to "fill up" with new positive thoughts. This can allow the negative thoughts to creep back in. Try to find new, wonderful thoughts about who you really are. Practice them every day. Here are some examples:

I deserve love and respect as I am.

Telling a lie puts the problem in the future. Telling the truth puts the problem in the past.

I welcome all my feelings, knowing they guide me to my true self.

I am trustworthy.

I can rely on me.

I say "yes" only when I mean it.

I say "no" when I feel it and mean it.

I am efficient and creative in my work.

I am lovable.

I invite friends to join me in simple pleasures.

I learn more about my value every day.

I will honor my mind, my body, and my spirit every day.

I will give myself respect and encouragement.

I will stand up for what I believe.

I will be honest to myself and other people.

I will care for myself.

I will forgive myself.

I'm beautiful inside and out.

# EIGHT IDEAS TO TRY TODAY

❖ **Accept yourself**. Healthy bodies come in all shapes and sizes. Focus on your good qualities and treat your body with respect and love. Remind yourself of all the things you are besides a body. Make a list of 10 or more qualities that make you GREAT.

❖ **Appreciate your body**. Reestablish a positive relationship with your body. Begin viewing your body as an instrument and not an ornament. Learn to appreciate your body for what it can do, not for what it looks like. Make a list of those things that your body does for you (e.g., breathing, walking, dancing, giving hugs, smiling, etc.).

❖ **Remember to follow your dreams**. Take time each day to remember what your dreams are. Write them down, make progress, and enjoy the journey.

❖ **Pamper your body**. Take a long hot bath and sooth yourself. Spoil yourself by getting a massage, making time for a nap, or finding a beautiful, quiet place to let your body relax every day.

❖ **Exercise**. Studies show that when people participate in even moderate exercise, such as walking, they feel more connected to and better about their bodies.

❖ **Think about the people you admire and look up to**. Consider whether their appearance was important to their success and accomplishments. You admire these individuals because of their contributions to your life, your community, and/or the world, not because of what they look like. Make a list of how you can work to be more like the traits that you admire in others. When you find yourself obsessing over appearance, try to work on one of the traits you admire in others.

❖ **Remind yourself that confidence is what is beautiful and sexy**, not a size, a shirt, or a pair of pants. Promise to keep your chin up today.

❖ **Surround yourself with support**. Seek out others in your life who value you for who you are and not for what you look like. Find people who exhibit a healthy relationship with their body. Surround yourself with people who remind you of your inner strength and beauty. Avoid those who tease or are constantly focusing on their weight.

# ARE YOU EXERCISE RESISTANT?

Do you hate exercise?
Do you do everything you can to avoid it?
Are you embarrassed to exercise?

You are not alone. Try this worksheet to discover what may be holding you back.

Explore the history of what may have happened to block your drive to have fun moving.

Ask yourself these questions:

What feelings or memories surface when you think of exercise? _____

_____

_____

When did exercise become a chore or requirement? _____

_____

_____

Do you connect exercise to losing weight or changing your shape; if so, how does that make you feel about exercise? _____

_____

_____

What connection does exercise have to your sexuality? _____

_____

_____

Did changes in your attitude toward exercise occur during puberty? _____

_____

_____

Were attitude changes related to sexual abuse, harassment, or feelings of sexual vulnerability? _____

_____

_____

How does exercise relate to your current view of you and your body? _____

_____

_____

Who are your fitness role models? _____

_____

_____

Think about what activity you enjoy doing. If you could do any physical movement you wanted, what would it be? _____

_____

_____

Imagine connecting with that activity. If you've always loved walking, don't think about getting on a treadmill. Instead, envision yourself hiking a trail surrounded by nature.

Get educated about exercise (e.g., find out what shoes are best for your chosen activity) and start moving.

(Adapted from Francie White, "Exercise Resistance in Women," audio cassette, 800-263-4217.)

# THERE'S A HOLE IN MY SIDEWALK:
## AUTOBIOGRAPHY IN FIVE SHORT CHAPTERS
## BY PORTIA NELSON

**Chapter 1**

I walk down the street.
There is a deep hole in the sidewalk.
I fall in.
I am lost . . . I am helpless.
It isn't my fault.
It takes forever to find a way out.

**Chapter 2**

I walk down the street.
There is a deep hole in the sidewalk.
I fall in again.
I can't believe I am in this same place.
But, it isn't my fault.
It still takes a long time to get out.

**Chapter 3**

I walk down the street.
There is a deep hole in the sidewalk.
I see it is there.
I still fall in . . . it is a habit . . . but my eyes are open.
I know where I am.
It is my fault. I get out immediately.

**Chapter 4**

I walk down the same street.
There is a deep hole in my sidewalk.
I walk around it.

**Chapter 5**

I walk down another street.

# HOW TO TALK
# WITH KIDS

PART

4

# HELPING CHILDREN

Mommy, does my butt look fat in these jeans?" asked 7-year-old Shannen. Her mother was shocked to hear her daughter's question. Her mother gave me a call, and I gave her a copy of "Savannah's Story" that you read in Part I of this workbook. It is included again here as an aid for working with children.

\* \* \*

## SAVANNAH'S STORY

One Saturday morning, Star looked in the mirror. Star is a big, beautiful Great Dane. She has long legs and strong muscles, is athletic, and is quite fun. But, Star looked in the mirror and saw a dog that was too big, too fat, and had an ugly coat. She was sad. She started feeling bad about herself when she began watching television and reading fashion magazines. None of the dogs on television looked like her. All the dogs on the television programs and in the fashion magazines were Chihuahuas. They all looked glamorous in beautiful outfits and diamond collars. They went to the coolest dog parks in the world and their owners always seemed to give them lots of attention. Star felt that if she could lose enough weight to be as small as the Chihuahuas on television, she too could have the diamond collar, beautiful clothes, great dog park vacations, and unlimited love.

On the other side of town, Jane also was looking in the mirror. Jane is a Chihuahua like the ones on television and in the magazines. She and Star are great friends. She has the diamond collar and beautiful clothes, but she is still unhappy. She does not like herself very much. She feels like her family buys her fancy clothes to hide the fact that she does not have long, flowing hair like her friend, Savannah. Savannah is a Maltese and has long, pretty white hair. Her family brushes her all the time and puts pretty bows in her hair. Jane feels that others pay Savannah more attention because she has that long, pretty hair. Jane thinks her life would be better if she could get hair extensions. She thinks that when she gets hair extensions, others will find her beautiful and want to play with her more.

Savannah, the Maltese, is quite happy. She does not watch the television shows about the "perfect" size, "perfect" hair, "perfect" clothes, "perfect" vacation, "perfect" family, or "perfect" friends. She knows that her family loves her, and she enjoys just being herself. Sure, sometimes things are hard for her, too. Her legs are very short, and her long hair makes her hot and often gets tangled. Her family does not make an issue of the things about herself that she finds challenging. Instead, they find ways to make her feel special. They take her for walks, play with her, and give her special treats. Savannah also has decided not to get upset. Instead, she chooses to focus on how great her family is and how much she loves them. She also feels lucky to have great friends. Her best friends are Star and Jane.

Savannah is excited to see her friends Star and Jane in the park for their Sunday play date. When Savannah saw Star and Jane lying sadly in the park, she playfully jumped on them and asked what was wrong. Star said that she was hungry. She was on a diet so that she could just get a little smaller and her family would then buy her a beautiful collar and coat. She said, "My family just doesn't like to pay attention to such a big dog." Jane piped up and said, "I know, I just want longer hair because my family would then be happier, like me more, and pet me more. I just can't stand my short hair." Savannah looked at her friends and said, "Star, you are so strong, athletic, fun, and a great listener. Jane, you are so funny, you speak English and Spanish, and you are great at snuggling. I wish that you two would focus on what is great about you rather than what the television and magazines tell you is popular. I miss the beauty that comes from you two accepting yourselves. And, besides, who really decides what is beautiful? Beautiful is not about a shape, a size, a color, a hairstyle, or your clothes. If there is one thing that I do know, it is that beauty lies in finding happiness inside yourself and sharing it with others. We all have our own different ways of bringing happiness to others, and it is unfair to yourself and the world not to be who you really are."

Star struggled, but stopped watching the television shows and reading the magazines that showed that being smaller and having nice stuff would make her happy. She paid attention to what she did well and soon found herself having fun again. She started smiling again when she realized she was strong, a good runner, and had great friends. Jane realized that she had been the only one thinking that she was not beautiful. She allowed herself to know that she did not need long hair to be loved and for others to find her beautiful. Her soul began smiling again. And, when their souls smiled again, they brought happiness to their friends and family who spread happiness to their friends and family who spread happiness to their friends and family until it spread to you today.

Look inside yourself to find what makes you special and beautiful. Be proud of who you are. Let your soul smile. Then you too will bring happiness to your friends and family who make up our world. We are all from different backgrounds and are different "breeds." Embrace your history and who you are.

\* \* \*

I shared with Shannen's mom how important it is to focus on Shannen's positive qualities versus her weight. Shannen and her mom then decided that every morning Shannen would tell her mom what was fabulous about Shannen instead of just what she was worried about.

# IF YOUR CHILD IS OVERWEIGHT . . .

- Many overweight children who are still growing will not need to lose weight but can reduce their rate of weight gain so that they can "grow into" their weight more healthily.

- Your child's diet should be safe and nutritious. It should include all of the Recommended Dietary Allowances (RDAs) for vitamins, minerals, and protein and contain the foods from the major Food Guide Pyramid groups. Any weight loss diet should be low in calories (energy) only, not in essential nutrients.

- Even with extremely overweight children, weight loss should be gradual.

- Crash diets and diet pills can compromise growth and are not recommended by most health care professionals.

- Weight lost during a diet frequently is regained unless children are motivated to change their eating habits and activity levels for a lifetime.

- Weight control must be considered a lifelong effort.

- Any weight management program for children should be supervised by a physician.

## SURGEON GENERAL'S SUGGESTIONS FOR OVERWEIGHT KIDS

- Let your child know he/she is loved and appreciated whatever his/her weight. An overweight child probably knows better than anyone else that he/she has a weight problem. Overweight children need support, acceptance, and encouragement from their parents.

- Focus on your child's health and positive qualities, not your child's weight.

- Try not to make your child feel different if he/she is overweight but focus on gradually changing your family's physical activity and eating habits.

- Be a good role model for your child. If your child sees you enjoying healthy foods and physical activity, he/she is more likely to do the same now and for the rest of his/her life.

- Realize that an appropriate goal for many overweight children is to maintain their current weight while growing normally in height.

- Be physically active. It is recommended that Americans accumulate at least 30 minutes (adults) or 60 minutes (children) of moderate physical activity most days of the week. Even greater amounts of physical activity may be necessary for the prevention of weight gain, for weight loss, or for sustaining weight loss.

- Plan family activities that provide everyone with exercise and enjoyment.

- Provide a safe environment for your children and their friends to play actively; encourage swimming, biking, skating, ball sports, and other fun activities.

- Reduce the amount of time you and your family spend in sedentary activities, such as watching TV or playing video games. Limit TV time to less than 2 hours per day.

## MORE SURGEON GENERAL'S SUGGESTIONS

- Many people focus on eating low-fat. This often leads people to eat no fat, which can lead to the thinking that all fat is bad—or even that fat people are lazy and bad.

- Don't focus on the idea that some foods are "good" and some are "bad"—when the focus should be eating in moderation.

- Weight gain is normal during adolescence. Girls grow 10 inches and gain 40 to 50 pounds from age 12 to 14. Boys grow 12 inches and gain 50 to 60 pounds.

- Is it any wonder that prepubescent children—whose bodies may become chubby as a natural part of maturing—fail to see their value in any other terms apart from physical appearance?

- The weight gain and height growth are not always perfectly synchronized and many adolescents experience periods of "chubbiness."

- The family's reaction to having a "chubby child" can be crucial in how adolescents view their worth for many years to come. Reports by adults who were put on diets by their parents during adolescence (and younger) are far too frequent. Since 90 to 98 percent of diets fail, you can imagine that dieters often end up feeling like failures.

- Children who are valued for their performance and looks rather than for who they are often struggle with eating disorders.

- Women and girls with eating disorders have historically outnumbered men and boys 9 to 1. However, it is now reported that the largest emerging group affected by these devastating diseases is young boys.

- Young athletes often practice unhealthy dieting habits in order to meet the standards for their sports. Sixty percent of all models and ballerinas have an eating disorder.

## TALKING TO KIDS ABOUT BEING OVERWEIGHT

- Talk to your kids about natural differences in body shapes and sizes. Statements by a father such as, "your mother is fat" . . . "you need to lose weight or you will look like her" or "why can't you wear something like that?" can be very damaging.

- Educate children about the ugliness of prejudice and teach them how to prevent it and fight it.

- Avoid negative attitudes or conversations about weight.

- Do not overemphasize beauty and body shape in your goals and dreams for your child.

- Don't discourage activities, such as swimming or dancing, just because they draw attention to weight or body shape.

- Talk to your kids about the misguided way in which appearance is linked to success.

- Be a good role model by eating nutritious meals and exercising regularly.

- Take other people seriously for who they are and what they do and not just on how slender or attractive they appear.

- Help children understand that one does not have to be slender to be seen as powerful, popular, or successful.

# TOP 10 REASONS TO GIVE UP DIETING

**#10:** Diets don't work. Even if you lose weight, you probably will gain it all back, and you might gain back more than you lost.

**#9:** Diets are expensive. If you didn't buy special diet products, you could save enough to get new clothes, which would improve your outlook right now.

**#8:** Diets are boring. People on diets talk and think about food and practically nothing else. There's a lot more to life.

**#7:** Diets don't necessarily improve your health. Like the weight loss, health improvement is temporary. Dieting actually can cause health problems.

**#6:** Diets don't make you beautiful. Very few people will ever look like models. Glamour is a look, not a size. You don't have to be thin to be attractive.

**#5:** Diets are not sexy. If you want to be more attractive, take care of your body and your appearance. Feeling healthy makes you look your best.

**#4:** Diets can turn into eating disorders. The obsession to be thin can lead to anorexia, bulimia, binging, and compulsive exercising.

**#3:** Diets can make you afraid of food. Food nourishes and comforts us, and gives us pleasure. Dieting can make food seem like an enemy and can deprive you of all the positive things about food.

**#2:** Diets can rob you of energy. If you want to lead a full and active life, you need good nutrition and enough food to meet your body's needs.

And the number one reason to give up dieting:

**#1:** Learning to love and accept yourself just as you are will give you self-confidence, better health, and a sense of well-being that will last a lifetime.

# PARENTS AND FRIENDS PREVENTING EATING DISORDERS

1. Consider your own attitudes and behaviors regarding your own body and then educate your children about the genetic basis for body shape and size. No two people are exactly alike. Talk to children about the ugliness of prejudice.

2. Do not overemphasize beauty and body shape in your goals and dreams for your child.

3. Be a good role model with regard to sensible eating, exercise, and self-acceptance. Avoid talking about food as "good/low-fat" or "bad/fattening." Emphasize the importance of eating a variety of foods that are well-balanced, three times a day.

4. Stop avoiding activities that draw attention to your weight and shape such as swimming. Avoid wearing clothes just to hide your weight.

5. Exercise for the health benefits of it and not as a compensation for the number of calories you've eaten.

6. Take other people seriously for who they are and what they do and not just for how slender or attractive they appear.

7. Help children understand that one does not have to be slender to be seen as powerful, popular, or successful.

8. Discuss and educate your children about prejudice and how to prevent it.

9. Encourage your children to be active and enjoy their physical capabilities without attention to their caloric intake (unless recommended by their doctor).

10. Promote self-esteem and self-respect in all endeavors. Give girls and boys the same opportunities without gender bias.

RESOURCES

## ORGANIZATIONAL RESOURCES

**National Eating Disorder Association Information and Referral Program**
603 Stewart Street, Suite 803, Seattle, WA 98101
1-800-931-2237
(206) 382-3587
(206) 829-8501 (fax)
Website: www.nationaleatingdisorders.org
Email: info@nationaleatingdisorders.org

**Academy for Eating Disorders**
6728 Old McLean Village Drive, McLean, VA 22101-3906
(703) 556-9222
(703) 556-8729 (fax)
Website: www.aedweb.org

**Behavioral Medicine**
Stanford Outpatient Psychiatry
401 Quarry Road, Stanford, CA 94305
(650) 498-9111

**Center for Overcoming Problem Eating and Eating Disorders Clinic**
Western Psychiatric Institute and Clinic
3811 O'Hara Street, Pittsburgh, PA 15213
(412) 624-5420

**Eating Disorders Clinic**
New York Psychiatric Institute
1051 Riverside Drive, NYSPI Unit 98, New York, NY 10032
(212) 543-5739

**Eating Disorder Research Program, University of Minnesota**
2701 University Avenue SE, Suite 206, Minneapolis, MN 55414
(612) 627-4494

**Renfrew Center**
475 Spring Lane, Philadelphia, PA 19128
1-800-736-3739

**Renfrew Center**
7700 Renfrew Lane, Coconut Creek, FL 33073
1-800-332-8415
Website: www.renfrew.org

**Remunda Ranch Arizona**
Box 2481 Jack Burden Road, Wickenburg, AZ 85358
1-800-445-1900

**Rutgers Eating Disorders Clinic**
GSAPP, Rutgers University, Box 819, Piscataway, NJ 08854
(732) 445-2292

**Center for Eating and Weight Disorders**
San Diego State University
6495 Alvarado Road, Suite 200, San Diego, CA 92120
(619) 594-3254

**Weight and Eating Disorders Program**
University of Pennsylvania
3600 Market Street, Philadelphia, PA 19104
(215) 898-7314

**Yale Center for Eating Disorders Program**
Yale University, Department of Psychology
P.O. Box 208205, New Haven, CT 06520-8205
(203) 432-4610

**Eating Disorder Program**
Adolescent and Young Adult Medical Group
Children's Hospital at Strong
610 Elmwood Avenue, Box 690, Rochester, NY 14642
(716) 275-7844

**Child and Adolescent Eating Disorders Programs**
Menninger Clinic
P.O. Box 829, Topeka, KS 66601-0829
1-800-351-9058

**Lifespan Weight Management Programs**
The Miriam Hospital Center for Behavioral and Preventive Medicine
164 Summit Avenue, Providence, RI 02906
1-800-927-1230

**National Institute for Mental Health (NIMH)**
Office of Communications and Public Liaison
Public Inquiries: (301) 443-4513
Media Inquiries: (301) 443-4536
E-mail: nimhinfo@nih.gov
Website: http://www.nimh.nih.gov

**American Anorexia Bulimia Association, Inc.**
(212) 575-6200
Website: http://www.aabainc.org

**Eating Disorders Awareness and Prevention, Inc.**
1-800-931-2237
Website: http://www.edap.org

**Harvard Eating Disorders Center**
1-888-236-1188, ext. 100
Website: http://www.hedc.org

**National Association of Anorexia Nervosa and Associated Disorders**
(847) 831-3438
Web site: http://www.anad.org

**Albert Ellis Institute**
45 East 65th Street, New York, NY 10021.
1-800-323-4738
Website: http://www.rebt.org

**Beck Institute**
GSB Building
City Line and Belmont Avenues, Suite 700, Bala Cynwyd, PA 19004-1610
(610) 664-3020
Website: http://www.beckinstitute.org

**National Association of Cognitive-Behavioral Therapists.**
P.O. Box 2195, Weirton, WV 26062
1-800-853-1135
Website: http://www.nacbt.org

**Eating Disorder Referral and Information Center**
2923 Sandy Pointe, Suite 6, Del Mar, CA 92014-2052
(858) 481-1515
  Answering any questions you might have about eating disorders and their prevention.

**National Eating Disorders Association (NEDA) (formerly EDAP & AABA)**
603 Stewart Street, Suite 803, Seattle, WA 98101-1264
1-800-931-2237
(206) 382-3587
(206) 829-8501 (fax)
  The National Eating Disorders Association is the largest nonprofit organization in the U.S. dedicated to expanding public understanding of eating disorders and promoting access to quality treatment for those affected along with support for their families through education, advocacy, and research. To achieve our mission, we have developed prevention programs for a wide range of audiences, we publish and distribute educational materials, we operate the nation's first toll-free eating disorders information and referral line at 1-800-931-2237, and we continually work to change the cultural, familial, and interpersonal factors that contribute to the development of eating disorders.

**National Association of Anorexia Nervosa and Associated Disorders (ANAD)**
Box 7, Highland Park, IL 60035
(847) 831-3438
> An association that is concerned with and provides a wide variety of programs for the entire Eating Disorders field (consumer advocacy, counsel, education, referral list, research, etc.).

**Eating Disorders Anonymous (EDA)**
18233 N. 16th Way, Phoenix, AZ 85022
> A fellowship of individuals who share their experience, strength, and hope with each other that they may solve their common problems and help others recover from their eating disorders. People can and do fully recover from having an eating disorder. In EDA, we help one another identify and claim milestones of recovery.

**Academy for Eating Disorders (AED)**
6728 Old McLean Village Drive, McLean, VA 22101
(703) 556-9222
> Promotes effective treatment and prevention initiatives, and stimulates research. AED sponsors an international conference.

**The Elisa Project**
8600 NW Plaza Drive, Suite 2B, Dallas, Texas 75225
(214) 369-5222
> To be a cohesive resource in providing eating disorder sufferers with a better chance of a cure. We accomplish this by educating health professionals, parents, children, the community, and the funding community.

**National Eating Disorders Screening Program (NEDSP)**
> NEDSP represents the first large scale screening for eating disorders. The program includes an educational presentation on eating disorders and/or related topics (body image, nutrition, etc.), a written screening test, and the opportunity to meet one-on-one with a health professional. It also provides individuals with information about how to help friends or family members who may be suffering from an eating disorder.

**National Center for Overcoming Overeating**
P.O. Box 1257, Old Chelsea Station, New York, NY 10113-0920
(212) 875-0442
> Women's campaign to end body hatred and dieting.

## Alliance for Eating Disorders Awareness

P.O. Box 13155, North Palm Beach, FL 33408-3155

(561) 841-0900

Seeks to establish easily accessible programs across the nation that allow children and young adults the opportunity to learn about eating disorders.

## Eating Disorders Coalition

609 10th Street NE, Suite #1, Washington, DC 20002

(202) 543-3842

To promote, at the federal level, further investment in the healthy development of children and all at risk for eating disorders, recognition of eating disorders as a public health priority, and commitment to effective prevention and evidence-based and accessible treatment of these disorders.

## Eating Disorders Council of Long Island (EDCLI)

50 Charles Lindbergh Blvd., Suite 400, Uniondale, NY 11553

(516) 229-2393

The EDCLI is a non-profit organization devoted to prevention, education, and support: prevention of eating disorders, education about eating disorders, and support to sufferers of eating disorders, their families, and their friends.

## Harvard Eating Disorders Center (HEDC)

356 Boylston Street, Boston, MA 02118

1-888-236-1188

A national non-profit organization dedicated to research and education, seeking to expand knowledge about eating disorders, their detection, treatment, and prevention.

## Massachusetts Eating Disorders Association, Inc. (MEDA)

92 Pearl Street, Newton, MA 02158

(617) 558-1881

Newsletter, referral network, and local support groups.

## Healing Connections, Inc.

1461A First Ave., Suite 303, New York, NY 10021

(212) 585-3450

A non-profit 501(c)(3) tax-exempt organization that strives to save lives through education, prevention, intervention, advocacy, and future financial assistance for people suffering from Anorexia and Bulimia.

## Overeaters Anonymous

P.O. Box 44020, Rio Rancho, New Mexico 87124-4020

(505) 891-2664

(505) 891-4320 (fax)

> Dealing with the issues of Compulsive Overeating. Site contains information on OA, information for healthcare professionals, a meeting locator map, fact file, OA literature, upcoming events, and more.

## The National Eating Disorder Information Centre (NEDIC)

CW 1-211, 200 Elizabeth Street, ES 7-421, Toronto, Ontario, M5G 2C4

(416) 340-4156

> A non-profit organization established in 1985 to provide information and resources on eating disorders and weight preoccupation.

## Eating Disorders Association of Manitoba

P.O. Box 34099, RPO Fort Richmond, Winnipeg, Manitoba R3T 5T5

(204) 275-3732

> A provincial non-profit organization founded in April of 1998 to provide support for individuals who have a loved one that suffers from an eating disorder.

## Eating Disorders Association (UK)

First Floor, Wensum House, 103 Prince of Wales Road, NORWICH, NR1 1DW, Norfolk, UK

01-603-621-414

> Offers understanding and support to sufferers and their families involved with the problems of Bulimia and Anorexia Nervosa.

## Somerset & Wessex Eating Disorders Association

Strode House, 10 Leigh Road

STREET, Somerset, BA16 0HA

> or

18-25 Project, 20A High Street

GLASTONBURY, Somerset, BA6 9DU

01-458-448-600

> Providing support to those affected by eating disorders; core services include telephone helpline and support groups.

**Sylfiderne (The Sylphs)**
c/o Elsebeth Sos Hansen,
Max Müllers Gade 11, 3.
DK-8000 Aarhus C
(+45) 40 60 59 54

> The Sylphs is a non-profit, non-religious, and non-party-political association that organizes people with an overeating disorder (that is eating for comfort and compulsive eating) and other people who sympathize with the objects of our association and who will work in its spirit.

**The Eating Disorders Action Group**
150 Bedford Highway, #2614
Halifax, NS B3M 3J5
(902) 443-9944

> The Eating Disorders Action Group is a community based, charitable organization dedicated to promoting healthy body image and self-esteem and to supporting individuals who experience disordered eating.

**WINS (We Insist on Natural Shapes)**
P.O. Box 19938, Sacramento, CA 95819
1-800-600-WINS

> A nonprofit organization dedicated to educating adults and children about what normal, healthy, shapes are, the dangers of eating disorders, and excessive dieting.

**ANAB Quebec**
114 Donegani Boulevard, Pointe Claire, Quebec H9R 2V4
(514) 630-0907

> ANAB Quebec is a Montreal-based non-profit organization that has been working since 1984 to help those whose lives are touched by an eating disorder.

**Asociación civil de Lucha contra Desórdenes Alimentarios**
(en español)
+54 627 22580/24290/24291 Int 211
Sector Desórdenes Alimentarios
5600 - San Rafael (Mendoza)
República Argentina
e-mail: aclda@bigfoot.com

> El objetivo de A.L.D.A. es ser útil, y brindar información y apoyo para prevenir y curar.

**Food Addicts Anonymous**
(To find a local group visit the website or call the World Service Office at (561) 967-387.)
National Food Addicts Anonymous Homepage (Information about the FAA recovery program, worldwide events, on-line meetings, tools for recovery, 12 steps and 12 traditions, and much more.)

**HUGS International Inc.**
Contact: Linda Omichinski, RD
linda@hugs.com
The center for information and resources about nondieting for adults and teens. We offer worldwide support and programs for people seeking a lifestyle without diets.

**Eating Disorders Association Resource Center**
The Eating Disorders Association is based in Queensland, Australia. It is an organization of people concerned about the growing prevalence and seriousness of eating disorders in our society.

**Eating Disorders Association**
Bryson House, 38 Ormeau Road, Belfast 7, IRELAND
Sackville Place, 44 Magdalen Street, Norwich, Norfolk NR3 1JE.
Tel: 080 232 234914
Members all receive information about Eating Disorders, including the magazine Signpost.

**Hazelden Ireland**
P.O. Box 616, Cork
Literature available on how to cope with eating disorders, 12-step recovery program, etc.

**Eating Disorders Association of WA (Western Australia)**
Unit 13A, Wellington Fair, 4 Lord Street, Perth
WESTERN AUSTRALIA 6000
Tel: 9221 0488
Fax: 9221 0499
Center for the Study of Anorexia and Bulimia
1 West 91st Street, New York, NY 10024
(212) 595-3449
The Center has four objectives: effective treatment, specialized training, significant research, and increased community understanding.

**British Columbia Eating Disorders Association**
841 Fairfield Road
Victoria BC Canada
(250) 383-2755
> Non-profit organization dedicated to peer support, peer counseling, and advocacy. We also run prevention programs for elementary schools, secondary schools, and university/college classes. We are completely volunteer driven and supported!

**Compulsive Eaters Anonymous—H.O.W.**
P.O. Box 4403, 10016 Pioneer Blvd Suite 101, Santa Fe Springs, CA 90670
(310) 942-8161
(310) 948-3721 (fax)
> A 12-step recovery program.

**Eating Disorders Professionals (IAEDP)**
123 NW 13th St. #206, Boca Raton, FL 33432-1618
1-800-800-8126
(407) 338-9913 (fax)
> An organization providing education, newsletters, local chapters, monthly bulletins, regional workshops, and certification. Professional membership.

**Promoting Legislation & Education About Self-Esteem, Inc. (PLEASE)**
91 S Main Street, West Hartford, CT 06107
(860) 521-2515
> Memberships and educational programs, workshops, and local chapters. Watchdog of the growing diet industry.

**National Association to Advance Fat Acceptance, Inc. (NAAFA)**
P.O. Box 188620, Sacramento, CA 95818
1-800-442-1214
> Advocacy group promoting size acceptance. Membership newsletters, educational materials, regional chapters, yearly convention, and pen-pal program.

# WEB RESOURCES

www.somethingfishy.com

www.eating-disorders.com

www.kidshealth.org

www.mirror-mirror.org

www.nationaleatingdisorders.com

www.edauk.com

www.anred.com

www.raderprograms.com

www.mentalheatlhscreening.com

www.gurze.net

www.athealth.com

www.EDreferral.com

www.about-face.org

www.wpic.pitt.edu

www.region.peel.on.ca/health/

www.pbskids.org

www.advocate4youth.com

www.shadesofhope.com

www.webmd.com

# PRINT RESOURCES

American Psychiatric Association. (1994). *Diagnostic and statistical manual of mental disorders* (4th ed.) (DSM-IV). Washington, DC: Author.

American Psychiatric Association Work Group on Eating Disorders. (2000). Practice guideline for the treatment of patients with eating disorders (revision). *American Journal of Psychiatry, 157* (1 Suppl.): 1–39.

Andersen, A. E. (1995). Eating disorders in males. In K. D. Brownell & C. G. Fairburn (Eds.), *Eating disorders and obesity: A comprehensive handbook* (pp. 177–187). New York: Guilford Press.

Becker, A. E., Grinspoon, S.K., Klibanski, A., Herzog, D. B. (1999). Eating disorders. *New England Journal of Medicine, 340* (14), 1092–1098.

Bruce, B., Agras, W. S. (1992). Binge eating in females: A population-based investigation. *International Journal of Eating Disorders, 12,* 365–373.

Cash, T. F. (1995). *What do you see when you look in the mirror?* New York: Bantam Books.

Chernin, K. (1982). *The obsession: Reflections on the tyranny of slenderness.* New York: Harper & Row.

Enright, S. (1997, June). Cognitive behaviour therapy. *British Medical Journal, 314* (7097), 1811–1816.

Fairburn, C. G. (1995). *Overcoming binge eating.* New York: Guilford Press. This book discusses who binges and why, how binging differs from overeating, and how a binge eater can gain control. It presents a step-by-step program for overcoming binge eating.

Freeman, R. (1988). *Body love: Learning to like our looks and ourselves.* New York: Harper & Row.

Goisman, R. M. (1997, May). Cognitive-behavioral therapy today. *Harvard Mental Health Letter 13* (11), 4–7.

Greenberger, D., & Padesky, C. (1995). *Mind over mood: A cognitive therapy treatment manual for clients.* New York: Guilford Press.

Grilo, C. M. (1988). The assessment and treatment of binge eating disorder. *Journal of Practical Psychiatry and Behavioral Health, 4,* 191–201. This article, written for health professionals, reviews the literature on binge eating disorder with a particular focus on its assessment and treatment. Implications for practice and future research are discussed.

Hirschmann, J. R., & Munter, C. H. (1995). *When women stop hating their bodies.* New York: Fawcett Columbine.

Hutchinson, M. G. (1985). *Transforming body image: Learning to love the body you have.* Berkeley, CA: The Crossing Press.

Maine, M. (2000). *Body wars: Making peace with women's bodies.* Carlsbad, CA: Gurze Books.

Orbach, S. (1986). *Hunger strike: The anorectic's struggle as a metaphor for our age.* New York: Norton Books.

Pipher, M. (1994). *Reviving Ophelia: Saving the selves of adolescent girls.* New York: Random House, Ballantine Books.

Shulman, E. (1994, January). Confessions of a Binge Eater. *Cincinnati Magazine.*

Siegel, M., Brisman, J., & Weinshel, M. (1997). *Surviving an eating disorder: New perspectives and strategies for family and friends.* New York: HarperCollins. This book discusses family therapy, psychopharmacology, hospitalization policies, insurance coverage, and support services for binge eating disorder patients and their families.

Spitzer, R. L., Yanovski, S., Wadden, T., Wing, R., Marcus, M. D., Stunkard, A., Devlin, M., Mitchell, J., Hasin, D., & Horne, R. L. (1993). Binge eating disorder: Its further validation in a multisite study. *International Journal of Eating Disorders, 13* (2), 137–153.

Stunkard, A. J. (1959). Eating patterns and obesity. *Psychiatric Quarterly, 33,* 284–295. This classic paper provides one of the first descriptions of binge eating in obese individuals.

Sullivan, P. F. (1995). Mortality in anorexia nervosa. *American Journal of Psychiatry, 152* (7), 1073–1074.

Wolf, N. (1991). *The beauty myth.* New York: Doubleday.

The Women's Therapy Centre Institute. (1994). *Eating problems: A feminist psychoanalytic treatment model.* New York: Basic Books.

Yanovski, S. Z. (1993). Binge eating disorder: Current knowledge and future directions. *Obesity Research, 1* (4), 306–323. This review of existing research on binge eating disorder, geared to health professionals, describes treatment methods, discusses their effectiveness, and recommends that doctors treating obese patients be aware of the disorder.

# RESOURCES BY TOPIC

## Adolescents and Eating Disorders

American Psychiatric Association. (1994). *Diagnostic & statistical manual of mental disorders* (4th ed.) (DSM-IV). Washington DC: Author.

Goodman, E. T., Mellin, L. M., Irwin, C. E., & Scully, S. (1992). Disordered eating characteristics in girls: A survey of middle class children. *Journal of the American Dietetic Association, 92,* 851–853.

The pressure to be perfect. (1986, January). *Glamour,* 154–181.

Rosen, J. C., & Gross, J. (1987). Prevalence of weight-reducing & weight-gaining in adolescent girls and boys. *Health Psychology, 6,* 131–147.

Sardula, et al. (1993). Weight control practices of U. S. adolescents and adults. *Annals of Internal Medicine, 119* (7), 667–677.

Swedish Medical Center / Seattle. (1996). *Bulimia: Eating yourself sick.* Northfield, MN: Life Skills Education.

## Dieting and Eating Disorders

Graves, L. (1988). *Why diets don't work: Narratives.* Wellesley, MA: National Eating Disorders Screening Program.

Johnson & Connors. (1987). *The etiology and treatment of bulimia nervosa.* Northvale, NJ: Jason Aronson.

Kurth, C. L., Krahn, D.D., Nairn, K., & Drewnowski, A. (1995). The severity of dieting and binging behaviors in college women: Interview validation of survey data. *Journal of Psychiatric Research, 29* (3), 211–225.

National Institute of Health Technology Assessment Conference Panel. (1992). Methods for voluntary weight loss and control. *Annals of Internal Medicine, 116,* 942–949.

Shisslak, C. M., Crago, M., & Estes, L. S. (1995). The spectrum of eating disturbances. *International Journal of Eating Disorders, 18* (3), 209–219.

## **Body Image, the Media, and Eating Disorders**

Loewy, M. I. (1988). Suggestions for working with fat children in the schools. *Professional School Counseling, 1* (4),18–22.

Smolak, L. (1996). *Next door neighbors: Eating disorders awareness and prevention puppet guide book.* Seattle, WA: National Eating Disorders Association.

Spitzer, R. L., Devlin, M. J., Walsh, B. T., Hasin, D, Wing, R. R., Marcus, M. D., Stunkard, A., Wadden, T. A., Agras, W. S., Mitchell, J., & Nonas, C. (1992). Binge eating disorder: A multisite field trial for the diagnostic criteria. *International Journal of Eating Disorders, 11,* 191–203.

Spitzer, R. L., Yanovski, S., Wadden, T., Wing, R., Marcus, M. D., Stunkard, A., Devlin, M., Mitchell, J., & Hasin, D. (1993). Binge eating disorder: Its further validation in a multisite study. *International Journal of Eating Disorders, 13,* 137–154.

Wurtman, J. (1992, November). "Why you can't stop eating." (radio interview, WCPO TV).

# BIBLIOGRAPHY

(Bibliography is courtesy of www.about-face.org.)

Abrams, K. K., Allen, L., & Gray, J. J. (1993). Disordered eating attitudes and behaviors, psychological adjustment, and ethnic identity: A comparison of Black and White female college students. *International Journal of Eating Disorders, 14,* 49–57.

Akan, G. E., & Grilo, C. M. (1995). Sociocultural influences on eating attitudes and behaviors, body image, and psychological functioning: A comparison of African-American, Asian-American, and Caucasian college women. *International Journal of Eating Disorders, 18* (2), 181–187.

American Association of University Women (1990). *Shortchanging girls, shortchanging America: Full data report.* Washington, DC: American Association of University Women.

American Psychiatric Association. (1994). Diagnostic and statistical manual of mental disorders (4th ed.). Washington, DC: Author. Anderson, A. E., & DiDomenico, L. (1992). Diet vs. shape content of popular male and female magazines: A dose-response relationship to the incidence of eating disorders? *International Journal of Eating Disorders, 11* (3), 283–287.

Andersen, A. & Holman, J.E. (1997). Males with eating disorders: Challenges for treatment and research. *Psychopharmacology Bulletin, 33* (3), 391–397.

Attie, I., & Brooks-Gunn, J. (1989). Development of eating problems in adolescent girls: A longitudinal study. *Developmental Psychology, 25,* 70–79.

# Bibliography

Bandura, A., & Walters, R. H. (1963). *Social learning and personality development.* New York: Holt, Rinehart & Winston.

Bartky, S. L. (1988). Foucault, femininity, and the modernization of patriarchal power. In I. Diamond, & L. Quinby (Eds.), *Feminism and Foucault: Reflections on resistance* (pp. 61–886). Boston: Northeastern University Press.

Basow, S. A., & Braman, A. C. (1998). Women and body hair: Social perceptions and attitudes. *Psychology of Women Quarterly, 22,* pp.637–645

Becker, A. E., & Hamburg, P. (1996). Culture, the media, and eating disorders. *Harvard Review of Psychiatry, 4,* 163–167.

Beren, S. E., & Chrisler, J. C. (1990). Gender role, need for approval, childishness, and self-esteem: Markers of disordered eating? *Research Communications in Psychology, Psychiatry and Behavior, 15,* 183–198.

Berg, F. M. (1997). Three major U.S. studies describe trends. *Healthy Weight Journal, 11* (4), 67–74.

Bergeron, S. M., & Senn, C. Y. (1998). Body image and sociocultural norms: A comparison of heterosexual and lesbian women. *Psychology of Women Quarterly, 22,* pp.385–401.

Berry, J. W., Trimble, J. E., & Olmedo, E. L. (1986). Assessment of acculturation. In W. J. Lenner & J. W. Berry (Eds.), Field methods of cross-cultural research (pp. 291–349). Beverly Hills, CA: Sage Bordo, S. (1993). *Unbearable weight.* New York: Berkley Publishing Group.

Bordo, S. (1993). *Unbearable weight.* New York: Berkley Publishing Group.

Brody, L. (1995, November). Are we losing our girls? *Shape,* pp. 94–98.

Brown, L. & Rothblum, E. (Eds.) (1989). *Overcoming Fear of Fat.* Harrington Park Press.

Button, E. J., & Whitehouse, A. (1981). Subclinical anorexia nervosa. *Psychological Medicine, 11,* 509–516.

Cash, T. F., & Henry, P. E. (1995). Women's body images: The results of a national survey in the U.S.A. *Sex Roles, 33* (1/2), 19–28.

Cash, T. F. & Pruzinsky, T. (Eds.) (1990). *Body Images: Development, Deviance and Change*. New York: Guilford Press.

Cash, T. F., Winstead, B. W., & Janda, L. H. (1986). The great American shape-up: Body image survey report. *Psychology Today, 20* (4), 30–37.

Cogan, J. C., Bhalla, S. K., Sefa-Dedeh, A., & Rothblum, E. D. (1996). A comparison study of United States and African students on perceptions of obesity and thinness. *Journal of Cross-Cultural Psychology, 27* (1), 98–113.

Collins, J. K., Beumont, P. J., Touyz, S. W., Krass, J., Thompson, P., & Philips, T. (1987). Variability in body shape perception in anorexic, bulimic, obese and control subjects. *International Journal of Eating Disorders, 6,* 633–638.

Cook, K. (1996). *Real gorgeous*. New York: W. W. Norton & Company, Inc.

Cooper, P. J., Taylor, M. J., Cooper, Z., & Fairburn, C. G. (1987). The development and validation of the body shape questionnaire. *International Journal of Eating Disorders, 6,* 485–494.

Counts, C. R., & Adams, H. (1985). Body image in bulimic, dieting, and normal females. *Journal of Psychopathology and Behavioral Assessment, 7* (3), 289–301.

Crago, M., Shisslak, C. M., & Estes, L. S. (1996). Eating disturbances among American minority groups: A review. *International Journal of Eating Disorders, 19* (3), 239–248.

Davis, C., & Katzman, M. (1999). Perfection as acculturation: Psychological correlates of eating problems in Chinese male and female students living in the Unites States. *International Journal of Eating Disorders, 25* (1), 65–70.

Dittrich, E. A. (1997). Sociocultural factors that influence body image satisfaction in women. (Doctoral Dissertation, California Institute of Integral Studies, 1997.) *Dissertation Abstracts International*.

Dolan, B., Birtchnell, S., & Lacey, J. H. (1987). Body image distortion in non-eating disordered women and men. *Journal of Psychosomatic Research, 31* (4), 513–520.

Dolan, B. (1991). Cross-cultural aspects of anorexia nervosa and bulimia: A review. *International Journal of Eating Disorders, 10* (1), 67–81.

Evans, C & Dolan, B. (1993). Body shape questionnaire: Derivation of shortened "alternate forms." *International Journal of Eating Disorders, 13* (3), 315–321.

Eating Disorder Referral and Information Center
International Eating Disorder Referrals
2923 Sandy Pointe, Ste 6, Del Mar, CA 92014
Website: www.EDReferral.com, email: edreferral@aol.com

Fabian, L. J., & Thompson, J. K. (1989). Body image and eating disturbance in young females. *International Journal of Eating Disorders, 8* (1), 63–74.

Fallon, P., Katzman, M. A., & Wooley, S. C. (Eds.). *Feminist Perspectives on Eating Disorders.* New York: The Guilford Press.

Fairburn, C. G., & Garner, D. M. (1986). The diagnosis of bulimia nervosa. *International Journal of Eating Disorders, 10,* 67–79.

Fairburn, C. G., & Garner, D. M. (1988). Diagnostic criteria for anorexia nervosa and bulimia nervosa: The importance of attitudes to weight and shape. In D. M. Garner & P. E. Garfinkel (Eds.), *Diagnostic issues in anorexia nervosa and bulimia nervosa* (pp. 36–55). New York: Brunner/Mazel.

Fernandez, F., Probst, M., Meerman, R., & Vandereycken, W. (1994). Body size estimation and body dissatisfaction on eating disorder patients and normal controls. *International Journal of Eating Disorders, 16* (3), 307–310.

Festinger, L. (1954). A theory of social comparison processes. *Human Relations, 7,* 117–140.

Fisher, M., Golden, N. H., Katzman, D. K. (1995). Eating disorders in adolescents: A background paper. *Journal of Adolescent Health, 16,* 420–437.

Franko, D. L. & Herrera, I. (1997). Body image differences in Guatemalan-American and White college women. Eating Disorders: *The Journal of Treatment and Prevention, 5* (2), 119–127.

Fraser, L. (1997). *Losing it: America's obsession with weight and the industry that feeds on it.* New York: Penguin Books.

Fredrickson, B.L. and Roberts, T-A (1997). Objectification theory: Toward under-standing women's lived experience and mental health risks. *Psychology of Women Quarterly, 21* (n2), pp.173–206.

Fredrickson, Roberts, et. al. (1998). That swimsuit becomes you: Sex differences in self-objectification, eating and math performance. *Journal of Personality & Social Psychology, 75* (n1), pp. 269–284.

Furnham, A., & Greaves, N. (1994). Gender and locus of control correlates of body image dissatisfaction. *European Journal of Personality, 8,* 183–200.

Gard, M. C. E., Freeman, C.P. (1996). The dismantling of a myth: A review of eat-ing disorders and socioeconomic status. *International Journal of Eating Disorders, 20* (1), 1–12.

Garner, D. M. (1997, January/February). The 1997 body image survey results. *Psychology Today,* pp. 31–44, 75–84.

Garner, D. M., Olmstead, M. P., & Polivy, J. (1983). Development and validation of a multidimensional eating disorder inventory for anorexia nervosa and bulim-ia. *International Journal of Eating Disorders, 2* (2), 15–34.

Garner, D. M., Olmstead, M. P., Polivy, J., & Garfinkel P. E. (1984). Comparison between weight- preoccupied women and anorexia nervosa. *Psychosomatic Medicine, 46,* (3), 255–266.

Geller, J., Johnston, C., Madsen, K., Goldner, E. M., Remick, R. A., & Birmingham, C. L. (1998). Shape- and weight-based self esteem and the eating disorders. *International Journal of Eating Disorders, 24* (3), 285–298.

Goldman, E. L. (1996). Eating disorders on the rise in preteens, adolescents. *Psychiatry News, 24* (2), 10.

Gortmaker, S. L., Must, A., Perrin, J. M., Sobol, A., & Dietz, W. H. (1993). Social and economic consequences of overweight in adolescence and young adult-hood. *New England Journal of Medicine, 329,* 1008–1012.

Gray, J. J., Ford, K., & Kelly, L. M. (1987). The prevalence of bulimia in a Black col-lege population. *International Journal of Eating Disorders, 6* (6), 733–740.

# Bibliography

Gregory, Deborah (1994, August). Heavy Judgment. *Essence,* pp.57–58, 105, 110–112 .

Grogan, S., Williams, Z., & Conner, M. (1996). The effects of viewing same-gender photographic models on body-esteem. *Psychology of Women Quarterly, 20* (4), 569–575.

Hall, A., & Hay, P. J. (1991). Eating disorder patient referrals from a population region 1977–1986. *Psychological Medicine, 21,* 697–701.

Hamilton, K., & Waller, G. (1993). Media influences on body size estimation in anorexia and bulimia: An experimental study. *British Journal of Psychiatry, 162,* 837–840.

Harris, S. M. (1994). Racial differences in predictors of college women's body image attitudes. *Women & Health, 21* (4), 89–103.

Harrison, A. G., & Stonner, D. M. (1976). Reference groups for female attractiveness among Black and White college females. In W. E. Cross (Ed.), *Third Conference on empirical research in Black psychology* (pp. 84–88). Washington, DC: US Department of Health, Education, and Welfare.

Heatherton, T. F., Nichols, P., Mahademi, Fary, & Keel, Pamela (1995). Body weight, dieting, and eating disorder symptoms among college students, 1981 to 1992. *American Journal of Psychiatry, 152* (11), 1623–1629.

Heatherton, T. F., & Polivy, J. (1992). Chronic dieting and eating disorders: A spiral model. In J. H. Crowther, D. L. Tennenbaum, S. E. Hobfold, & M. A. Parris (Eds.), *The etiology of bulimia nervosa: The individual and familial context.* Washington, DC: Hemisphere.

Heinberg. L. J., & Thompson, J. K. (1992). Social comparison: Gender, target importance ratings, and relation to body image disturbance. *Journal of Social Behavior and Personality, 7* (2), 335–344.

Heinberg, L. J., Thompson, J. K., & Stormer, S. (1995). Development and validation of the sociocultural attitudes towards appearance questionnaire. *International Journal of Eating Disorders, 17* (1), 81–89.

Herzog, D. B. (1984). Are anorexic and bulimic patients depressed? *American Journal of Psychiatry, 141,* 1594–1597.

Hesse-Biber, S. (1996). *Am I thin enough yet?* (pp. 44–57). New York: Oxford University Press.

Hill, A. J., & Pallin, V. (1998). Dieting awareness and low self-worth: Related issues in 8-year-old girls. *International Journal of Eating Disorders, 24* (4), 405–413.

Hirschmann, J. R. & Munter, C. H. (1997). *When Women Stop Hating Their Bodies.* Fawcett Books.

Irving, L. M. (1990). Mirror images: Effects of the standard of beauty on the self- and body-esteem of women exhibiting various levels of bulimic symptoms. *Journal of Social and Clinical Psychology, 9* (2), 230–242.

Irving, L. M., Riddle, M., Berel, S., Cannon, R., Bower, Z., & Parks, C. (1997). Sociocultural contributors to disordered eating in adult women. Poster presented at the 1997 annual convention of the American Psychological Association, Chicago, IL.

Jacobson, M. F., & Mazur, L. A. (1996). *Sexism and sexuality in advertising. In Marketing Madness* (pp.75–87). Boulder: Westview Press, Inc.

Jeffery, R. W., & French, S. A. (1996). Socioeconomic status and weight control practices among 20- to 45-year-old women. *American Journal of Public Health, 86* (7), 1005–1010.

Johnston, J. (1994). *Appearance Obsession.* Health Communications.

Johnson, J., Tobiu, D., & Lipkin, J. (1989). Epidemiologic changes in bulimic behavior among female adolescents over a five-year period. *International Journal of Eating Disorders, 6,* 647–655.

Joiner, G. W., & Kashubeck, S. (1996). Acculturation, body image, self-esteem, and eating-disorder symptomatology in adolescent Mexican American women. *Psychology of Women Quarterly, 20* (3), 419–435.

Kalodner, C. R. (1997). Media influences on male and female non-eating disordered college students: A significant issue. *Eating Disorders: The Journal of Treatment and Prevention, 5* (1), 47–57.

Kaz-Cooke (1996). *Real Gorgeous.* W. W. Norton & Company.

Keys, A., Brozek, J., Henschel, A., Mickelsen, O., & Taylor, H. L. (1950). *The biology of human starvation.* Minneapolis: University of Minnesota Press.

Kilbourne, Jean (1994). Still killing us softly: Advertising and the obsession with thinness. In Fallon, P., Katzman, M. A., & Wooley, S. C. (Eds.), *Feminist Perspectives on Eating Disorders* (pp. 395–418). New York: The Guilford Press.

Klesges, R. C., & Klesges, L. M. (1988). Cigarette smoking as a dieting strategy in a university population. *International Journal of Eating Disorders, 7* (3), 413–419.

Koenig, L., & Wasserman, E. L. (1995). Body image and dieting failure in college men and women: Examining links between depression and eating problems. *Sex Roles, 32* (3/4), 225–249.

Kog, E., & Vandereycken, W. (1989). Family interaction in eating disorder patients and normal controls. *International Journal of Eating Disorders, 8* (1), 11–23.

Kohn, M., & Schooler, C. (1983). *Work and personality: An inquiry into the impact of social stratification.* Norwood, NJ: Ablex.

Kuczmarski, R. J., Flegal, K. M., Campbell, S. M., & Johnson, C. L. (1994). Increasing prevalence of overweight among US adults. *Journal of the American Medical Association, 272* (3), 205–211.

le Grange, D., Stone, A. A., & Brownell, K. (1998). Eating disturbances in white and minority female dieters. *International Journal of Eating Disorders, 24* (4), 395–403.

le Grange, D, Telch, C. F. & Agras, W. S. (1997). Eating and general psychopathology in a sample of Caucasian and ethnic minority subjects. *International Journal of Eating Disorders, 21* (3), 285–293.

le Grange, D., Telch, C. F. & Tibbs, J. (1998). Eating attitudes and behaviors in 1,435 South African Caucasian and non-Caucasian college students. *American Journal of Psychiatry,155* (2), 250–254.

Lee, S. (1993). How abnormal is the desire for thinness? A survey of eating attitudes and behaviour among Chinese undergraduates in Hong Kong. *Psychological Medicine, 23,* 437–451.

Lee, S., Leung, T., Lee, A. M., Yu, H., & Leung, C. M. (1996). Body dissatisfaction among Chinese undergraduates and its implications for eating disorders in Hong Kong. *International Journal of Eating Disorders, 20* (1), 77–84.

Lester, R., & Petrie, T. A. (1998). Physical, psychological, and societal correlates of bulimic symptomatology among African American college women. *Journal of Counseling Psychology, 45* (3), 315–321.

Lester, R., & Petrie, T. A. (1998). Prevalence of disordered eating behaviors and bulimia nervosa in a sample of Mexican American female college students. *Journal of Multicultural Counseling & Development, 26* (3), 157–165.

Lester, R., & Petrie, T. A. (1995). Personality and physical correlates of bulimic symptomatology among Mexican American female college students. *Journal of Counseling Psychology, 42* (2), 199–203.

Levine, M. P., & Smolak, L. (1997). Media as a context for the development of disordered eating. In L. Smolak, M. P. Levine, & R. Striegel-Moore (Eds.), *Developmental Psychopathology of Eating Disorders* (pp.235–257). Mahwah, New Jersey: L. Erlbaum Associates.

Levine, M. P., Smolak, L., & Hayden, H. (1994). The relation of sociocultural factors to eating attitudes and behaviors among middle school girls. *Journal of Early Adolescence, 14* (4), 471–490.

Lucas, A. R., Beard, C. M., O'Fallon, W. M., & Kurland, L. T. (1991). 50-year trends in the incidence of anorexia nervosa in Rochester, Minn.: A population-based study. *American Journal of Psychiatry, 148* (7), 917–922.

Matsuura, K., Fujimura, M., Nozawa, Y., Iida, Y., & Hirayama, M. (1992). The body preference of Japanese female students. *International Journal of Obesity, 16,* 87–93.

McCarthy, M. (1990). The thin ideal, depression and eating disorders in women. *Behavioural Research Therapy, 28* (3), 205–215.

McKinley, N. M., & Hyde, J. S. (1996). The objectified body consciousness scale. *Psychology of Women Quarterly, 20* (2),181–215.

Mellin, L. M., Scully, S., & Irwin, C. E. (1986). *Disordered eating characteristics in preadolescent girls.* Meeting of the American Dietetic Association, Las Vegas, (Abstract).

Mendoza, R., & Martinez, J. L. (1981). The measurement of acculturation. In A. Baren, Jr. (Ed.), *Explorations in Chicano Psychology* (pp.21–82). New York: Holt. Minuchin, S., Rosman, B., & Baker, L. (1978). Psychosomatic families: Anorexia nervosa in context. Cambridge, MA: Harvard University Press.

Moreno, A., & Thelen, M. H. (1993). Parental factors related to bulimia nervosa. *Addictive Behaviors, 18,* 681–689.

Murray, S. H., Touyz, S. W., & Beumont, Peter, J. V. (1995). The influence of personal relationships on women's eating behavior and body satisfaction. *Eating Disorders: The Journal of Treatment and Prevention, 3* (3), 243–252.

Murray, S. H., Touyz, S. W., & Beumont, Peter, J. V. (1996). Awareness and perceived influence of body ideals in the media: A comparison of eating disordered patients and the general community. *Eating Disorders: The Journal of Treatment and Prevention, 4* (1), 33–46.

Myers, P. N., Jr., & Biocca, F. A. (1992). The elastic body image: The effect of television advertising and programming on body image distortions in young women. *Journal of Communications, 42* (3), 108–133.

Neumark-Sztainer, D., Butler, R., & Palti, H. (1995). Eating disturbances among adolescent girls: Evaluation of a school-based primary prevention program. *Journal of Nutrition and Education, 27,* 24–31.

Nylander, I. (1971). The feeling of being fat and dieting in a school population: Epdemiologic, interview investigation. *Acta Sociomedica Scandinavica, 3,* 17–26.

Olmedo, E. L., & Padilla, A. M. (1978). Empirical and construct validation of a measure of acculturation for Mexican Americans. *The Journal of Social Psychology, 105,* 179–187.

Orenstein, P. (1994). *School Girls.* New York: Doubleday.

Parker, S., Nichter, M., Nichter, M., Vuckovic, N., Sims, C., & Ritenbaugh, C. (1995). Body image and weight concerns among African American and White adolescent females: Differences that make a difference. *Human Organization, 54,* 103–114.

Pate, J. E., Pumariega, A. J., Hester, C., & Garner, D. M. (1992). Cross-cultural patterns in eating disorders: A review. *Journal of the American Academy of Child and Adolescent Psychiatry, 31* (5), 802–809.

Paxton, S. J., Wertheim, E. H. Gibbons, K, Szmukler, G. I. et al. (1991). Body image satisfaction, dieting beliefs, and weight loss behaviors in adolescent girls and boys. *Journal of Youth & Adolescence, 20* (3), 361–370.

Petrie, T. A. (1993). Disordered eating in female collegiate gymnasts: Prevalence and personality/attitudinal correlates. *Journal of Sport & Exercise Psychology, 15,* 424–436.

Petrie, T. A., Rogers, R., Johnson, C., & Diehl, N. (1996, August). *Development and validation of the beliefs about attractiveness scale-revised.* Paper presented at the American Psychological Association annual convention, Toronto, Canada.

Pike, K. M., & Rodin, J. (1991). Mothers, daughters, and disordered eating. *Journal of Abnormal Psychology, 100* (2), 198–204.

Pinhas, Leora; Toner, Brenda B.; Ali, Alisha; Garfinkel, Paul E.; and others (1999). The effects of the ideal of female beauty on mood and body satisfaction. *International Journal of Eating Disorders, 25* (2), 223–226.

Polivy, J., Garner, D. M., & Garfinkel, P. E. (1986). Causes and consequences of the current preference for thin female physiques. In C. P. Herman, M. P. Zanna, & E. T. Higgins (Eds.), *Physical appearance, stigma, and social behavior: The Third Ontario Symposium in Personality and Social Psychology* (pp.89–112). Hillsdale, NJ: Erlbaum.

Polivy, J., & Herman, C. P. (1983). *Breaking the diet habit.* New York: Basic Books.

Polivy, J., & Herman, C. P. (1987). Diagnosis and treatment of normal eating. *Journal of Consulting and Clinical Psychology, 55* (5), 635–644.

Polivy, J., & Herman, C. P. (1995). Dieting and its relation to eating disorders. In K. D. Brownell & C. G. Fairburn (Eds.), *Eating Disorders and Obesity: A Comprehensive Textbook for Eating Disorders and Obesity* (pp. 83–86).

Powell, A. S., & Kahn, A. S. (1995). Racial differences in women's desires to be thin. *International Journal of Eating Disorders, 17* (2), 191–195.

# Bibliography

Powers, P. D., & Erickson, M. T. (1986). Body-image in women and its relationship to self-image and body satisfaction. *The Journal of Obesity and Weight Regulation, 5* (1), 37–49.

Pumariega, A., Gustavson, C. R., Gustavson, J. C., Stone Motes, P., & Ayers, S. (1994). Eating attitudes in African-American women: The Essence eating disorders survey. *Eating Disorders: The Journal of Treatment and Prevention, 2* (1), 5–16.

Pyle, R. L., Neuman, P. A., Halvorson, P. A., & Mitchell, J. E. (1991). An ongoing cross-sectional study of the prevalence of eating disorders in freshman college students. *International Journal of Eating Disorders, 10* (6), 667–677.

Richins, M. L. (1991). Social comparison and the idealized images of advertising. *Journal of Consumer Research, 18,* 71–83.

Robinson, B. E., & Bacon, J. G. (1996). The if only I were thin . . . treatment program: Decreasing the stigmatizing effects of fatness. *Professional Psychology: Research and Practice, 27* (2), 175–183.

Rodin, J. (1992). *Body traps.* New York: William Morrow.

Rodin, J., Silberstein, L. R., & Striegel-Moore, R. H. (1984). Women and weight: A normative discontent. In T. B. Sonderegger (Ed.), *Nebraska Symposium on Motivation, Vol. 32, Psychology and Gender* (pp. 267–307). Lincoln: University of Nebraska Press.

Root. M. P. P. (1990). Disordered eating in women of color. *Sex Roles, 22* (7/8), 525–536.

Rosen, J. C.,Reiter, J., & Orosan, P. (1995). Cognitive-behavioral body image therapy for body dysmorphic disorder. *Journal of Consulting & Clinical Psychology, 63* (3), 437.

Rotter, J. B., Chance, J. E., & Phares, J. E. (1972). *Applications of a social learning theory of personality.* New York: Holt, Rinehart & Winston, Inc.

Rucker, C. E. & Cash, T. F. (1992). Body images, body-size perceptions, and eating behaviors among African-American and White college women. *International Journal of Eating Disorders, 12* (3), 291–299.

Schmidt, U. H., Troop, N. A. & Treasure, J. L. (1999). Events and the onset of eating disorders: Correcting an "age old" myth. *International Journal of Eating Disorders, 25* (1), 83–88.

Schreiber, G. B., Robins, M., Striegel-Moore, R., Obarzanek, E., Morrison, J. A., & Wright, D. J. (1996). Weight modification efforts reported by Black and White preadolescent girls: National Heart, Lung, and Blood Institute growth and health study. *Pediatrics, 98,* 63–70.

Shapiro, Laura. (1997, April). Is fat that bad? *Newsweek,* pp. 59–64.

Shisslak, C., Pazda, S., & Crago, M. (1990). Body weight and bulimia as discriminators of psychological characteristics among anorexic, bulimic and obese women. *Journal of Abnormal Psychology, 99,* 380–384.

Silverstein, B., Perdue, L., Peterson, B., Kelly, E. (1986). The role of the mass media in promoting a thin standard of bodily attractiveness for women. *Sex Roles, 14* (9/10), 519–532.

Silverstein, B., Peterson, B., & Perdue, L. (1986). Some correlates of the thin standard of bodily attractiveness for women. *International Journal of Eating Disorders, 5* (5).

Slade, P. D. (1988). Body image in anorexia nervosa. *British Journal of Psychiatry, 153* (Suppl. 2), 20–22.

Slade, P. D. (1994). What is body image? *Behavioral Research Therapy, 32* (5), 497–502.

Smith, D.E., Thompson, J. K., Raczynski, J. M.& Hilner, J. E. (1999). Body image among men and women in a biracial cohort: The CARDIA study. *International Journal of Eating Disorders, 25* (1), 71–82.

Smith, J. E., & Krejci, J. (1991). Minorities join the majority: Eating disturbances among Hispanic and Native American youth. *International Journal of Eating Disorders, 10* (2), 179–186.

Smolak, L., & Striegel-Moore, R. H. (1997). Developmental research and eating disorders. In L. Smolak, P. Levine, & R. Striegel-Moore (Eds.), *Developmental Psychopathology of Eating Disorders* (pp.183–203). Mahwah, New Jersey: L. Erlbaum Associates.

Sobal, J. (1995). Social influences on body weight. In K. D. Brownell & C. G. Fairburn (Eds.), *Eating disorders and obesity: A comprehensive textbook for eating disorders and obesity* (pp. 73–77).

Spitzack, C. (1990). *Confessing excess: Women and the politics of body reduction.* Albany: State University of New York Press.

Steiner-Adair, C. (1984). The body politic: Normal female adolescent development and the development of eating disorders. *Dissertation Abstracts International, 45,* 1925–1926. (University Microfilms International No. 8421207).

Steiner-Adair, C., & Purcell, A. (1996). Approaches to mainstreaming eating disorders prevention. *Eating Disorders: The Journal of Treatment and Prevention, 4* (4), 294–309.

Stice, E. (1994). Review of the evidence for a sociocultural model of bulimia nervosa and an exploration of the mechanisms of action. *Clinical Psychology Review, 14* (7), 633–661.

Stice, E., Nemeroff, C., & Shaw, H. E. (1996). Test of the dual pathway model of bulimia nervosa: Evidence for dietary restraint and affect regulation mechanisms. *Journal of Social and Clinical Psychology, 15* (3), 340–363.

Stice, E., Schupak-Neuberg, E., Shaw, H. E., & Stein, R. I. (1994). Relation of media exposure to eating disorder symptomatology: An examination of mediating mechanisms. *Journal of Abnormal Psychology, 103* (4), 836–840.

Stice, E., & Shaw, H. E. (1994). Adverse effects of the media portrayed thin-ideal on women and linkages to bulimic symptomatology. *Journal of Social and Clinical Psychology, 13* (3), 288–308.

Stice, E., Ziemba, C., Margolis, J., & Flick, P. (1996). The dual pathway model differentiates bulimics, subclinical bulimics, and controls: Testing the continuity hypothesis. *Behavior Therapy, 27,* 531–549.

Story, M., French, S. A., Resnick, M. D., & Blum, R. W. (1995). Ethnic/racial and socioeconomic differences in dieting behaviors and body image perceptions in adolescents. *International Journal of Eating Disorders, 18* (2), 173–179.

Striegel-Moore, R.H., Silberstein, L. R., Frensch, P., & Rodin, J. (1989). A prospective study of eating among college students. *International Journal of Eating Disorders, 8* (5), 499–509.

Striegel-Moore, R. H., McAvay, G., & Rodin, J. (1986). Psychological and behavioral correlates of feeling fat in women. *International Journal of Eating Disorders, 5,* 935–947. Striegel-Moore, R. H.,

Schreiber, G. B., Pike, K. M., Wilfley, D. E., & Rodin, J. (1995). Drive for thinness in black and white preadolescent girls. *International Journal of Eating Disorders, 18* (1), 59–69.

Striegel-Moore, R. H., Silberstein, L. R., & Rodin, J. (1986). Toward an understanding of sociocultural risk factors for bulimia. *American Psychologist, 41,* 246–263.

Striegel-Moore, R. H., & Smolak, L. (1997). The role of race in the development of eating disorders. In L. Smolak, M. P. Levine, & R. Striegel-Moore (Eds.), *Developmental psychopathology of eating disorders* (pp.259–284). Mahwah, New Jersey: L. Erlbaum Associates.

Thelen, M. H., & Cormier, J. F. (1995). Desire to be thinner and weight control among children and their parents. *Behavior Therapy, 26,* 85–99.

Thomas, V. G. (1988). Body-image satisfaction among Black women. *The Journal of Social Psychology, 129* (1), 107–112.

Thompson, B. (1996). Multiracial feminist theorizing about eating problems: Refusing to rank oppressions. *Eating Disorders: The Journal of Treatment and Prevention, 4* (2), 104–114.

Thompson, J. K., Fabian, L. J., Moulton, D. O., Dunn, M. E., & Altabe, M. N. (1991). Development and validation of the physical appearance related teasing scale. *Journal of Personality Assessment, 56* (3), 513–521.

Thompson, J. K., Heinberg, L. J., Altabe, M., & Tantleff-Dunn, S. (1999). *Exacting Beauty: Theory, Assessment, and Treatment of Body Image Disturbance.* Washington, DC: American Psychological Association.

Thompson, J. K., Heinberg, L. J., & Tantleff, S. (1991). The physical appearance comparison scale (PACS). *The Behavior Therapist, 14,* 174.

## Bibliography

Thompson, M., & Schwartz, D (Winter, 1982). Life adjustment of women with anorexia nervosa and anorexic-like behavior. *International Journal of Eating Disorders.*

Tiggeman, M., & Pickering, A. S. (1996). Role of television in adolescent women's body dissatisfaction and drive for thinness. *International Journal of Eating Disorders, 20* (2), 199–203.

Tiggeman, M., & Rothblum, E. D. (1988). Gender differences and social consequences of perceived overweight in the United States and Australia. *Sex Roles, 18* (1/2), 75–86.

U.S. Department of Health and Human Services. (September, 1993). 1991 National health interview survey. (CD ROM, #1771035). Washington, DC: National Center for Health Statistics.

Wadden, T. A., Brown, G., Foster, G. D., & Linowitz, J. R. (1991). Salience of weight-related worries in adolescent males and females. *International Journal of Eating Disorders, 10* (4), 407–414.

Waller, G., & Hamilton, K., & Shaw, J. (1992). Media influences on body size estimation in eating disordered and comparison subjects. *British Review of Bulimia and Anorexia Nervosa, 6* (2), 81–87.

Wertheim, E. H., Paxton, S. J., Schutz, H. K., & Muir, S. L. (1997). Why do adolescent girls watch their weight? An interview study examining sociocultural pressures to be thin. *Journal of Psychosomatic Research, 42* (4), 345–355.

Wilfley, D. E., Schreiber, G. B., Pike, K. M. Striegel-Moore, R. H., Wright, D. J., & Rodin, J. (1996). Eating disturbances and body image: A comparison of a community sample of adult Black and White women. International Journal of Eating Disorders, 20 (4), 377–387.

Wiseman, C.V., Gray, J.J.. Mosimann, J.E. & Ahrens, A.H. (1992). Cultural expectations of thinness in women: An update. *International Journal of Eating Disorders, 11* (1), 85–89.

Wolf, N. (1992). *The beauty myth.* New York: Doubleday.

Wooley, S.C., & Wooley, O.W. (1984, February). Feeling fat in a thin society. *Glamour,* 198–252.

Yoshimura, K. (1995). Acculturative and sociocultural influences on the development of eating disorders in Asian-American females. *Eating Disorders: the Journal of Treatment and Prevention, 3* (3), 216–228.

Youth Risk Behavior Surveillance-US, 1995. (1996, Sept. 27). Morbidity and Mortality Weekly Report, CDC, US Public Health Service. 45:SS-4:1–84.